MOUNTAIN GEOMORPHOLOGY:

GEOMORPHOLOGICAL PROCESSES IN THE CANADIAN CORDILLERA

B.C. GEOGRAPHICAL SERIES, NUMBER 14

edited by

H. OLAV SLAYMAKER
Associate Professor
Department of Geography
University of British Columbia

and

H.J. McPHERSON
Associate Professor
Department of Geography
University of Alberta

Tantalus Research Limited

Publisher - Vancouver, Canada

B. C. GEOGRAPHICAL SERIES, NUMBER 14

Editorial Address:
W. G. Hardwick, Ph.D.
Department of Geography
The University of British Columbia
Vancouver 8, B.C., Canada

409168
Coutts

Circulation Address:
P.O. Box 34248
Vancouver Postal Station "D"
2405 Pine Street,
Vancouver 9, B.C., Canada

Published at Vancouver, Canada

LIST OF CONTRIBUTORS

Boydell, A.N., Department of Geography, University of Calgary.

Chamberlin, T.W., Department of the Environment, Fisheries Service.

Day, T.J., Department of Geography, University of Canterbury, New Zealand.

Dingwall, P.R., Department of Geography, Queens University, Ontario.

Gardner, J., Department of Geography, University of Iowa.

Gilbert, R., Department of Geography, University of British Columbia.

Goodell, B.C., Faculty of Forestry, University of British Columbia.

Gray, J.T., Department of Geography, Laurentian University.

Harris, S.A., Department of Geography, University of Calgary.

Hewitt, K., Department of Geography, University of Toronto.

Hirst, F., Department of Geography, University of Ottawa.

Kellerhals, R., Department of Civil Engineering, University of Alberta.

Luckman, B.H., Department of Geography, University of Western Ontario.

McPherson, H.J., Department of Geography, University of Alberta.

O'Loughlin, C.L., Faculty of Forestry, University of British Columbia.

Owens, I.F., Department of Geography, University of Toronto.

Ponton, J.R., Department of Geography, University of British Columbia.

Ryder, J.M., Department of Geography, University of British Columbia.

Russell, S.O., Department of Civil Engineering, University of British Columbia.

Schaerer, P.A., National Research Council of Canada.

Shaw, J., Department of Geography, University of Alberta.

Slaymaker, H. Olav, Department of Geography, University of British Columbia.

Smith, D.G., Department of Geography, University of Calgary.

Woo, M., Department of Geography, University of British Columbia.

TABLE OF CONTENTS

INTRODUCTION

During the past decade increasing interest has been shown in the Canadian Cordillera as a research area (Figure 1). However, to date, no single book dealing with the geomorphology of the Canadian Cordillera per se has been produced. This series of articles written by researchers actively engaged in studies in the mountains of Alberta and British Columbia seeks to remedy this situation.

In collecting and preparing a reader of this nature two alternative courses of action were open to the editors. The publication could consist either of a series of previously published articles or it could contain research papers written specifically for it. The latter procedure was adopted as it was felt that more would be gained by publishing the results of new research than by reprinting papers already available elsewhere.

As no one series of papers can hope to encompass all aspects of mountain geomorphology the present collection is organised around five principal themes with an emphasis upon the operation of present day geomorphic processes. This emphasis is particularly evident in the sections on slopes and rivers. The themes, each of which is represented by a section in the book, include studies into the theoretical framework for mountain geomorphic investigations, glacial geomorphology, slope processes and form, fluvial processes and morphology and the environmental management of mountain regions.

Hewitt's paper, which is the only one in Section One, is an imaginative overview of the state of mountain geomorphology. In essence, it forms a theoretical framework for, and an introduction to, succeeding sections.

Section Two contains a number of studies relating to Pleistocene chronology and glacial geomorphic research. Shaw presents a critical analysis of the research on Quaternary chronologies developed for several areas along the eastern slopes of the Alberta Rockies while Harris and Boydell discuss in detail the glacial sequence of events in the mountain and foothills segments of the Bow and Red Deer river valleys. In an interesting article, Gardner describes the pattern of glacier retreat since Neoglaciation for a number of glaciers in Banff and Jasper National Parks and discusses some of the landforms created during the retreat phase. The final paper in the section, by Ryder, is an original synthesis of Pleistocene chronological and glacial geomorphic investigations in south western British Columbia.

Slope evolution and the operation of slope forming processes are central themes in geomorphology and mountain regions provide excellent natural laboratories for their study. The research reported in Section Three clearly illustrates the spectrum of studies underway in the Canadian Cordillera. An emphasis on the movement and nature of unconsolidated debris, with relatively little attention being directed to the processes by which debris arrives on the slopes is apparent. Three types of slopes are examined in the following series of papers: debris covered slopes (Dingwall and Owens), slopes of definite morphology such as talus cones (Gray and Luckman) and debris-covered mountain sides with a heavy vegetation cover and some soil development (Chamberlin and O'Loughlin).

Rates of talus accumulation on slopes in the central Yukon are presented by Gray. He shows that contemporary measured rates, although significant, cannot account for the post-glacial development of the talus cones he studied. Luckman directs attention to the significance of snow avalanches in the downslope movement of near-surface debris on talus cones. Owens' paper points to the importance of mudflow activity on debris covered slopes in high relief zones while O'Loughlin demonstrates that landslides are an extremely significant denudation process in the humid coastal forests of British Columbia. Both Owens and O'Loughlin use a similar research strategy and infer process from morphological evidence. Dingwall studies the process of overland flow in a small high altitude watershed near the Columbia Icefield and finds that appreciable amounts of fine sediment are moved downslope by slope wash. The subsurface migration of water is investigated by Chamberlin and his conclusions have important implications for the interflow of fine materials and moisture which may contribute to the initiation of landslides and mudflows.

Aspects of river behaviour, sediment transport and deposition in high mountain streams are outlined in Section Four. Two main groupings are evident: studies of stream flow mechanics and hydraulic geometry (Kellerhals, Day and Ponton) and studies of sediment transport and depositional morphology (McPherson and Hirst, Smith and Gilbert). Kellerhals summarises the flow characteristics of steep mountain rivers with frequent flow discontinuities and Day reviews the results of his study into the hydraulic geometry of small high energy mountain streams while Ponton

10

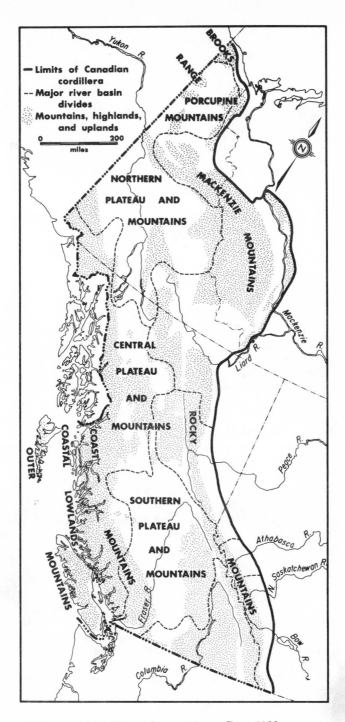

Figure 1 - The Canadian Cordillera

11

discusses the hydraulic geometry of two moderately large mountain rivers exhibiting continuous flow. Taken together, these contributions relate to gravel and boulder paved mountain channels that are not entirely free to determine their own form. The resulting hydraulic geometries are distinctive. McPherson and Hirst illustrate the changes in sediment character which occur over the surfaces of two alluvial fans in the upper North Saskatchewan valley in Alberta and conclude that alluvial fan formation in this area is primarily the result of fluvial deposition in the post-glacial period with mudflow action playing a minor role. Smith presents a preliminary report of a detailed study of channel hydraulics and morphology in a section of the upper North Saskatchewan River where an instructive variety of channel types occurs. Deltaic sedimentation in mountain lakes is another important feature of Cordilleran fluvial processes: the paper by Gilbert describes the hydrological and sedimentological conditions of the Lillooet River delta.

Management and the resource utilization of mountain areas is considered in the articles contained in Section Five. Three types of problem are considered: management of forested mountain basins (Goodell and Woo), distinctive hazards of high relief regions (Schaerer and Russell), and the role of geomorphological understanding in the applied river problems of the Cordillera (Kellerhals and Slaymaker). The usefulness of the simulation approach for snow storage prediction as developed by Woo forms a useful complementary study to that of Goodell, who uses the experimental watershed approach to determine ways of optimising basin yield. Schaerer discusses the ecology of snow avalanches and their control and Russell describes the effects of an extreme flood in a small mountain basin. Kellerhals itemises specific projects which are in progress in relation to hydrometric surveys, and river regime and sediment transport studies in the Alberta Rocky Mountains and Foothills, and, finally, Slaymaker considers the varying importance of geomorphological and land use factors at a number of discrete spatial scales in the sediment yield and control problems of the British Columbia part of the Cordillera.

Publication of this volume would not have been possible without the help, encouragement and financial support of many individuals and agencies. The editors are indebted to the various contributors for preparing their high calibre articles and for their promptness in submitting them. Primary editing of Section Three was carried out by Dr. J. S. Gardner of the University of Iowa and Section Four by Dr. M. A. Church of the University of British Columbia. Their skilled and careful editing is gratefully acknowledged, although the final form of the volume is the responsibility of the senior editors. Thanks are also extended to the Leon and Thea Koerner Foundation for contributing towards the cost of preparation of this reader.

H. Olav SLAYMAKER
University of British Columbia

H. J. McPHERSON
University of Alberta

SECTION   ONE

THEORETICAL   FRAMEWORK

Chapter 1-1

THE MOUNTAIN ENVIRONMENT AND GEOMORPHIC PROCESSES.

Ken Hewitt

Mountain landscapes have often been treated as a special field of geomorphological investigation. Work over the last couple of decades has certainly made great strides in the sophistication of tools and observations. Yet most of the major questions concerning mountain landforms remain as open as when they were formulated in the last century. It is the purpose here to review and restate those questions in contemporary terms, and especially in relation to studies of geomorphic processes.

Mountain landscapes are fascinating of themselves, but their greatest value for the study of geomorphic processes arises when we treat them in terms common to the whole range of sub-aerial conditions. In both their physical development and the measurement scales which describe them, mountains are essentially continuous with the rest of landscape. It is their relative rather than absolute conditions which are of geomorphological concern. In the present volume we are concerned with areas which combine high relief, steep slopes and altitudinally varying local climates. It is this combination, forming the truly mountain environment, which will be concentrated upon here, rather than the alpine morphogenetic context alone. Nevertheless, mountains and their geomorphic development are directly linked with lower relief areas of drainage basins and the debris loads of lowland rivers for example are often strongly dependent upon events in mountainous watersheds. Even the extensive plains of the Amazon or the Indo-Gangetic rivers are dominated in these respects by their Andean or Himalayan headwaters. Of course, where a mountain front rises abruptly from the plains a sharp break in the hydrologic and erosional conditions occurs, and is recorded in geomorphic processes and forms. Elsewhere, the progress from high to low relief is more gradual and so are its effects in geomorphic terms. The impact of critical thresholds of slope will be spread over a broad zone of gradually increasing mean slope angles.

One can usually define characteristic sets of forms and processes within a mountain area. Distinctive variants of particular processes arise, as with the subtle differences between frost climates or glaciation in different latitudinal zones. But in this

17

respect, mountain areas are as different from one another as from lowland areas. Overall then, we shall look at what is distinctive about mountain regions within the framework of the continuous spectrum of geomorphic conditions. With that in mind, the rest of this essay will focus upon two broad issues that relate mountain conditions to the rest of landscape. These are, the idea of a high energy condition, and the relation of distinctive morphological features to clima-geomorphic conditions and denudation history.

THE HIGH ENERGY CONDITION

Regional Rates of Net Erosion

In the context of geomorphic process studies, the mountain environment is often referred to as being a high energy situation. Evidently this means high energy relative to most other sub-aerial environments. In the global context denudation generally proceeds at its greatest rate in high relief areas (Corbel, 1959; Schumm, 1963). The amount of geomorphic work performed in moving debris through a range of altitude is normally greatest in the higher relief parts of drainage basins. There may be some other situations where erosional activity is even more vigorous, as on some coastlines, "badlands" or margins of continental ice-sheets (see Slaymaker: Section 5). Extreme hydrologic and atmospheric events in lowlands may equal in erosional impact the larger events in mountains. However, the vigour of erosion, and frequency of larger erosional events, is never so extensive and uniformly productive of high erosion rates as in mountains. There is strong evidence that the variation of erosion with relief has a larger range than that which occurs with differences in climate (Corbel, op. cit; Langbein and Schumm, 1958). In other words, the impact of high relief on erosion rates is greater than that of maximal rates associated solely with phyto-climatic zones. The globally maximal relief of the Greater Himalaya and Karakoram is associated with some of the highest recorded rates of regional denudation for large drainage basins. The values exceed 1 mm. yr^{-1} (0.04 in. yr^{-1}) for the Upper Indus (70,000 mi^2; 180,000 km^2) and Kosi (23,000 mi^2; 60,000 km^2) (Hewitt, 1967). Information from Alaskan mountains and the European Alps indicate rates in some cases exceeding 0.6 mm. yr^{-1} (0.02 in. yr^{-1}) while an actual rate of 0.6 mm. yr^{-1} (0.02 in. yr^{-1}) has been reported for a small basin in the Canadian Rocky Mountains (McPherson, 1971). If relief and dissection are of primary importance, it seems likely that the only other area where Himalayan levels of regional denudation will be found, is the eastern flank of the high Andes. Of course, regional rates of net erosion are crude measures of the energy conditions attending geomorphic processes.

18

The sources of the high energy condition have generally been identified as "relief energy" and extremes of climate. The positive mass of the solid earth above sea level represents gravitational potential energy derived from thos tectonic processes which govern the broad configuration and development of the crust. Moisture deposited at higher altitudes has greater potential energy. Yet positive mass and altitude are not themselves sufficient to produce vigorous geomorphic activity. Geomorphic conditions on the high plateau and interior basins of Central Asia, the North American Cordillera or the Altiplano of Andean South America are not equivalent to those of the true mountain areas which border them. More important than altitude is available relief. Either differential uplift must create steep mountain fronts or, as is more usual, the expenditure of positive mass must have proceeded to a point where dissection of the mountain block is fairly complete. The availability of potential energy for geomorphic processes depends most directly upon the local relief and distribution of slope angles. For a given range of altitude, it is the more thoroughly dissected mountains which exhibit the higher erosion rates. If we compare the hypsometry of the Pamirs and the Karakoram Himalaya the former are found to have greater positive mass. The latter is more deeply and widely dissected although having a greater array of high peaks and crest-lines. The two are broadly similar in glacierisation, total relief and climates. It seems, therefore, that degree of dissection explains the apparently much higher denudation rates for the Karakoram (see Hewitt, 1967).

The higher denudation rates referred to apply to yield of sediment in streams. The matter is more complicated in relation to mass movements. Spontaneous or weather-aided collapse of rock walls and talus are sensitive to what is called "over-steepening." In post-glacial periods, or epochs of rapid stream incision, steep rock walls are exposed and may be subject to a period of massive landslide activity. The net effect of such events may be to exceed the rates of denudation due to all other processes over much longer periods of time (see Jäckli, 1957; Oberlander, 1965; Appendix). Numerous examples of massive landslides in glacially over-steepened valleys are on record for western Canadian mountains as elsewhere (e.g. Mathews and McTaggart, 1969).

While relief and slope angles are of most direct significance in mountain erosion, climatic conditions also tend to enhance erosional energy. Albrecht Penck (1919) was one of the first to emphasize that alpine climates are high energy ones. Indeed, he believed that clima-geomorphic conditions become increasingly severe with altitude and create an upper limit to the possible height of mountains. We shall return to that point later. In considering the climatic environment alone, we must distinguish between the greater potential energy of moisture at higher altitude, and specifically the more extreme heat and moisture conditions. The latter derive both from increased local intensities and from the spatial and temporal variations that are a feature of mountain climates. The orographic effect on precipitation is one source of increased climatic energy. However, the increase of precipitation does not usually continue over altitudinal ranges greater than 7000 ft (2100 m) so that at very high altitudes there is a decrease of precipitation. Half of the mass of the atmosphere lies below 18,000 ft (5400 m) and more than half the mass of water vapour below 8500 ft (2550 m). While mountains tend to be local moisture traps, there is a greater potential for large fluctuations in humidity and insolation effects with altitude. Average wind velocities increase with altitude, a fact of particular importance in evaporation and the movement of snow and dust. Altitudinal range, aspect and slope angles all contribute to the strong spatial variations in mountain micro-climates.

Temporal fluctuations in weather and climate also tend to be greater in mountains. For a given geographic location there will be an altitudinal band of frequent temperature fluctuations across the freeze-thaw boundary. This band will change with weather conditions and migrate vertically according to season. In glacierized mountains, hydrologic regime and moisture availability in general have strongly seasonal fluctuations, compressing the discharge curves for given precipitation and thereby increasing the ability to erode and transport debris.

Mountains of the continental interiors, and those of great altitudinal range show huge contrasts in moisture availability, temperatures and phyto-geomorphic conditions. Since it is often the case that such mountains are more humid at higher elevation, erosion is enhanced as accumulated moisture moves downslope. In fact, though much of the literature emphasizes the contrasts between different mountain situations, the downslope continuity of erosional events is perhaps more important. Avalanching or vigorous solifluction on high slopes have powerful effects on lower slopes. Forest cover will often be severely reduced and the timber-line lowered by the spill-over from alpine processes into timbered areas. Avalanches become the sources of abundant moisture that trigger more forceful mass-movements such as debris and mudflows at lower altitudes. (See Luckman: Section 3; Schaerer: Section 5).

In narrow valleys with steep walls, the descent of land-slides, avalanches, and even tributary glaciers block streams and produces the devastating natural dam bursts recorded in most high mountain regions. In the broad perspective, such detailed events add to the high energy conditions, in this case through the downslope

20

continuities between clima-geomorphic zones. It seems that
overall, one can accept Penck's contention that mountain climates
are high energy ones. Since the evidence points to heavy avalanching
and glaciers as the largest producers of erosional debris in
mountains there may be some truth in his contention that severity
increases with altitude.

Magnitude and Frequency of Erosional Events

When we look for quantitative evidence of the power of
processes according to altitude and relief there is very little information. What we require are magnitude and frequency statistics
of erosional events. A time series of an appropriate kind indicates
the duration and relative frequencies of events of different magnitudes, and allows us to compare the effectiveness of varying energy
conditions. The issue most often discussed is the relative importance of frequent and rare events, the latter usually being of high
magnitude (Wolman and Miller, 1960). In terms of hydrology, it
has been suggested that as annual erosion is effected by fewer and
more intense events, so the role of rare events becomes greater.
Work on mountain geomorphology usually emphasizes the role of
short-lived high intensity events (Ichikawa, 1958; Rapp, 1960 b;
Veyret, 1959). Rapp's detailed work in Kärkevagge was somewhat
damaging to this view, in showing that the steady removal of solutes
was the most important process (Rapp, 1960 a). However, work in
the Karakoram indicates quite the opposite (Hewitt, 1967).
Avalanches are overwhelmingly important at high altitude; mudflows,
rock-slides and other rapid mass-movements are most important
below the snow line. Solutes are relatively unimportant in stream
transport, while suspended sediment transport is of major importance during floods. Obviously, there is need for caution in
generalizing among mountain areas. Nevertheless, the question
remains as to whether the increasing role of short-lived, high energy
events with increasing relief also means that rare events are more
important. Is there any reason why the magnitude-frequency curves
should not simply shift in magnitude? We lack the evidence to test
these ideas but it may be useful if a descriptive context is outlined.

We can begin by considering what happens to mass-movement processes on slopes as average slope angles are increased.
Some mountain landscapes are only marginally different from lower
relief areas. In such cases it seems that increasing relief and
slope may affect the rate at which processes operate without greatly
changing their character. The extent to which this is true will
depend upon the particular combination of lithology, vegetation,
climate and relief. However, in relation to these environmental
constraints, there are thresholds of relief and slope conditions
above which new kinds of processes appear. These thresholds are

21

of particular importance in mountain regions. Thus, the instability of regolith increases markedly as slopes approach the limiting angles of repose for regolith under stable environment. These angles usually lie somewhere between 25° and 45°. Since the environment is not stable, the strength of regolith materials fluctuates especially with changing moisture and temperature conditions. Fluctuating strength, local steepening due to removal of material, or the impact of movements from above will, where slopes are distributed close to the critical angle of repose, make the regolith subject to sudden failure. The nearer average slope is to the critical, the greater will be the role of rapid, short-lived mass movements. Similar "thresholds" are likely to relate to tree-line or the limit of continuous grass and shrub coverage; to the upper limit of regolith cover of any kind; to the different considerations of strength which obtain in hard rock, and finally, to the stability of snow and ice on slopes above the snow line. In general, it seems that the function of such thresholds in promoting sudden, rapid movements becomes greater with increasing slope. One can also say that the steeper the slope, usually the lower the grade of weathering necessary before material is entrained. The way in which characteristic slope angles relate to the stability of landscape materials is discussed in a later paragraph.

The momentum and distance of travel for high energy mass movements on steep slopes means that a relatively small number of small areal coverage is equivalent to a large area and frequent occurrence of slow mass movements. The work of Rapp (1960 a) and Luckman (1971) illustrates this point. Since increasing relief enhances the potential for rapid mass movements, they play a relatively larger role in mountains.

In the case of stream action any condition which compresses the discharge curve for a given volume of run-off will increase stream power. A large exponential increase in sediment transport with a relatively small exponential increase in water discharge is evident in most sediment rating curves. The general effect of mountain climates is to increase the range of moisture availability through time, in many cases producing the concentrated annual hydrograph of the glacial regime. Steep channels also tend to compress short-term hydrographs (see Kellerhals; Section 4). Compression of discharge curves seems to be a major factor in the higher sediment yields from extensively glacierised mountains in Alaska, the Alps and Himalaya (Corbel, op. cit.; Schumm, op.cit.). A good deal of the literature on mountain streams also emphasises the role of severe, short-lived floods due to snow-melt, heavy rains, or natural dam-bursts. For the Himalayan Indus, where 91% of the sediment yield is carried in just over two months, flows in excess of the partial duration series base (i.e. the annual

22

maximum flow with recurrence interval of 1.15 years) transport
about 25% of the total load. They represent about 3% of the once-
daily discharge record for the last hundred years, and consist of
flood waves averaging about five days in duration. The results
here, as for most mountainous rivers agree that: ". . . the more
variable the flow of the streams, the larger the percentage of load
. . . carried by relatively few isolated events or in relatively few
days . . . ." (Leopold, Wolman and Miller, 1964, p. 73). On the
other hand it is not clear that very rare events are any more significant than in low energy regions. The high energy condition is
reflected by the dominant role of a few, short-lived events but these
occur in nearly every year. Of course, we are not yet able to take
full account of the other element, the areal extent of the basins.
The Upper Indus is a gigantic basin and there is good reason to
believe that the averaging out of extreme events for the whole basin
is not the case for smaller tributaries. Until the relations between
extreme events and long-term records on the one hand, and basins
of equivalent size on the other, can be compared for highland and
lowland areas we cannot confidently predict the relative importance
of rare events in each case.

Energy in the Mountain Geomorphic System

While magnitude and frequency data for erosional events
offer an attractive avenue for examining effects of high energy
conditions, in another sense they are as unsatisfactory as net
denudation rates. The statistics represent the results rather than
the operation of the geomorphic controls and processes. The
physical relationship to the statistics to general landscape morphology
is quite tenuous. Meanwhile, along with the inherent complexities
of mountain environments, the conservative nature of adjustments
among elements of geomorphic systems, and the essentially energy-
dissipating nature of geomorphic processes must mean that output
from such systems is low in information. Since we are speaking in
terms of energy perhaps we should pause to consider some of its
properties.

One of the most difficult problems is to define geomorphic
systems in such a way that the quantities of energy and the way they
are budgeted become clearly formulated. Taking the most basic
terms, the energy of any physical system may be described by a
relation of the form:-

$$G = H - TS$$

where G is the free energy, H is the enthalpy or total energy, S is
the entropy and T the absolute temperature. As a general rule
entropy, (a measure of the energy not available to do work and

23

therefore a fundamental feature of the budgeting of energy) increases with total energy and mass. Matter must have the maximum randomness of distribution and thermal motion proper to its temperature, and within the constraints imposed by forces and structures built into the system. Unfortunately, these "forces and structures" become overwhelmingly important in certain systems, especially where one is greatly involved with solid matter as in geomorphology. The fact that all forms of energy, whether mechanical, chemical, thermal or electrical, can be converted to common units does not alter the inappropriateness of some of these forms of energy characterisation for given systems. Thus, we have suggested that geomorphic energy relates primarily to relief and slope angles, which determine the efficiency with which gravitational energy is converted to geomorphic work. However, gravitation is not associated with temperature and hence its entropy value is always zero. In terms of mechanical energy therefore, all the potential energy residing in the positive mass of a landscape is available to perform work. Further, while a free energy term can be associated directly with slope, relief and mass, an entropy term will be constant for these variables throughout a drainage basin. Thus the gravity model of a geomorphic system is unequivocal in attributing greatest erosional energy to more mountainous areas. It is also of virtually no assistance in showing why basins and slopes develop the forms we actually find, or budget mass and energy transfers in the ways they do.

However, we are much more interested in changes of state or energy distribution brought about by various processes. For processes at constant pressure and temperature our equation can be written:-

$$\Delta G = \Delta H - T \Delta S$$

A negative value of ΔG represents a loss of free energy as a result of the process, and is equal to the work it can perform. ΔG will be negative either if the total energy ΔH falls, or if ΔS increases. Unless energy is being pumped through a system from outside, any change in the system must lead to an increase in S. Energy will flow from higher to lower levels, and from "high order" energy such as gravitation to lower orders, in particular by a yield of heat from mechanical work. It is by analogy with the fact that a definable quantity of heat is evolved when, say, a mass of rock falls through a given distance, that we arrive at the model of landscape energy used by Leopold and Langbein (1962). They use temperature as an analogue of gravitational potential energy which enables them to treat an ideal river system as a thermodynamic engine. Hence, the rate of production of entropy by the geomorphic process is greatest in the higher and steeper parts of a basin. They

24

also conclude that their model shows the range of possible slopes to become greater with altitude above base level, and that the concave upward profile of rivers is analogous to a least work condition in mechanical systems. Their reasoning is attractive and their paper probably one of the most important in recent geomorphological literature. However, their emphasis is upon runoff with the implication that it accurately depicts what is happening to the essential element of landscape change, the movement of solid matter. Scheidegger (1970) has suggested that the real analogy with landscape is with mass rather than energy transfer processes, but shows that the results are entirely consistent with the thermodynamic scheme. Hence, our equation would take the form:-

$$\Delta S = \Delta M/h$$

where mass (M) is taken to be equivalent to available energy, and height (h) equivalent to temperature. This is directly applicable to the transfer of solid matter. However, it still does not deal with the role of that other congruent "system" the forces and structures present in rock and debris, and which geomorphologists call the "resisting forces." These may seem unimportant or to cancel out over an entire basin, but a study of the mountain landscape leads one to seek a more specific evaluation.

The solid matter of landscape enters our considerations of energy in two respects, first through the bonding energies in the rock materials and the energy exchanges of weathering, and secondly in terms of the geometric or structural effects of size, shape, sorting and roughness of surface materials. If a unit mass of rock of fixed strength moves over a slope of constant roughness, then the dissipation of energy can be said to increase with increasing speed of movement, and increasing area in contact with the surface. Hence we can say that, with these conditions steeper slopes will lead to greater rate of entropy production. Gravitational energy will be expended and degraded at a faster rate in mountains than in lowlands. But the conditions we have imposed do not normally apply. In the mountain situation rock and regolith are less weathered, and retain more of the order introduced by lithology. The forces present in the materials tend to resist disordering and dissipation of energy much more than in lowland areas. The greater proportion of deterministic elements in the slopes of mountain regions would seem to reflect this. It is generally believed that physical weathering is much more important in mountains than in lower areas. However, chemical weathering, which is mostly exothermic, is the greater dissipator of the bonding energies of rock materials. The final aspect which must be weighed here is the matter of surface roughness. Mountain debris, and the large areas of rock wall generally produce a rougher landscape than in lowlands. The

25

effect should be to increase surface friction, and hence the dissipation of heat from downslope movements. If we examine the contours in mountain regions, as we move down from the divide, undulations of successively larger amplitude and average wave-length assume greater importance. The effect is not only a result of the greater slice of landscape mass between contours of lower elevation. In general the higher frequency undulations are damped down at successively lower elevations. The impression is there-fore, that surface roughness of small and large scale tends to decrease downslope and hence, to be smaller where slopes are at lower angles.

In the drainage basin, it seems that as the erosional forces become greater, so do the resisting forces. What the mountain geomorphologist lacks at present is some effective way to model and measure the controlling effects of variations in material properties, slope and erosional energy upon the develop-ment of high relief landscapes. It may be merely a problem of viewing the appropriate physical considerations at the proper scale. For, on the largest scale the models of Langbein and Leopold and of Scheidegger do seem to apply. They emphasise as we did at the beginning, the continuity of landscape for the transfer of materials. Landscapes are open systems with respect to moisture and heat flux but for long periods are essentially closed in terms of rock mass. The solid matter of which the landscape is composed is gradually spread outwards from mountains to lowlands and sedi-mentary basins. The general form which such a diffusion of mass must take appears necessarily to be like the Davisian model (see Scheidegger, 1970, p. 275). Evidently, there is a tendency for those areas where weathering is least advanced, and/or slope and drainage processes most vigorous to offer greater resistance to erosion, and for the relative importance of material properties and their expression in landscape morphology to be greatest in higher energy areas. It still remains to be shown how we can express the driving and the resisting forces in ways which are locally useful to the student of mountain morphology and processes, but the terms of reference seem clear.

DISTINCTIVE MORPHOLOGIC FEATURES

As in most other areas of geomorphology, the bulk of the literature on mountain landscapes is concerned with distinctive visual or mappable forms. Explanations of these forms in terms of attendant processes vary widely. Some pertinent examples will be reviewed here, beginning with those of larger dimensions.

Accordant Erosion Surfaces

Breaks of slope, spurs, crest-lines, and summits that seem part of a continuous erosional envelope have been reported in most mountain areas. King (1967) makes considerable use of such "surfaces" in interpreting the large-scale erosional development of the earth. The evidence for these accordances, as they are called, has usually been visual. From high level viewpoints, extensive portions of the European Alps, the Himalaya, and the North and South American Cordilleras seem to form gipfelfluren or "peak plains." Other accordances are seen at lower levels. Without doubt, the eye exaggerates the phenomena. Distance and scale effects easily mask the true relief of apparent accordances. Nevertheless, objective sampling of heights on relief maps supports the belief in accordances or preferred elevations in some mountain areas. Interpretation of these accordances differs especially as to whether they represent temporal or merely spatial breaks in erosional conditions; and whether they are in some sense a normal or an accidental product of high relief environments.

The dominant school of thought considers accordances as representing breaks in erosional development through time. It is significant that exponents of this view invariably stress the horizontal extrapolation of accordant heights. Accordances are seen as remnants of planation controlled by earlier base levels (c.f. Davis, 1923; King, op. cit.). Erosional processes are seen as working to produce sub-horizontal surfaces and the presence of a relatively low-angle surface at high altitudes can only be explained as an interrupted cycle of development. Thus low-angle surfaces also become the main evidence used for tracing landscape development since they are the only strictly historical elements that can occur. For scholars of this bent, it is hard to see accordances as anything but part of a single envelope. If there is negligible landscape mass above the envelope it will be seen as a remnant of some near-complete cycle, -- an uplifted pene- or pedi-plain. Lower, less extensive surfaces will record the position of temporary base levels of incomplete cycles.

To the student of geomorphological processes the most unsatisfactory aspect of arguments like the above centres around the question of preservation. When erosional rates exceed 1 mm yr^{-1} (0.04 in. yr^{-1}) and erosional severity increases with altitude it is hard to believe in the survival of surfaces millions of years old. Also, we expect disturbances due to tectonic events to be propagated through the landscape as erosion proceeds. In this propagation it is the steeper rather than the lower angle surfaces of previous conditions, which are likely to be crucial. With so

27

many other sources of variance in rates of erosion in mountains, it seems unlikely that there will be a strong relationship between the altitude of some low-angle surfaces and distant historical events.

It is interesting that other scholars, who interpret accordances as a result of spatial variations in erosion, tend to emphasise the vertical aspect of accordances. Often the accordances are not considered as part of a continuous envelope even of altitudinal environment. The extreme case here is Daly's explanation of the formation of peak plains (Daly, 1905). He saw the high level accordance as simply a side-effect of regularly spaced drainage channels, with valley slopes intersecting to form approximately uniform watersheds. The results of morphometric analyses of drainage networks make Daly's model entirely plausible, as does the visual appearance of many mountain regions from high flying aircraft or satellites. Although stressing the vertical aspect of accordance, Albrecht Penck's idea of a "limiting climate" would seem to be unrelated to Daly's model, in spite of a recent attempt to link the two (Thompson, 1962). Penck's idea that mountains will be truncated at a particular level by the extreme severity of clima-geomorphic conditions cannot be taken quite literally. Otherwise Everest, or the highest mountain in each climatic zone would be the only relevant cases. Rather, we must think in terms of powerful alpine processes which tend to consume high crest-lines and peaks relatively quickly. Initially, the processes create accordances of alpine slopes, and may also act to produce a peak plain, somewhat after the manner of Daly's streams, by controlling the form of high rock walls. Since the alpine processes are the more vigorous they should consume salients quickly, leaving the alpine slopes to form a summit envelope. Clearly, this interpretation is of direct interest to the student of contemporary geomorphological processes. He need hardly deny the possibility of other mechanisms, or consider those advanced as mutually exclusive possibilities. Yet there is nothing in our knowledge of the interrelations between the elements of climate and geomorphic processes that is inconsistent with the production of accordances by these alone. In the elaboration of the Penckian idea of a limiting climate, what concerns us is how the relative power of erosional processes and the slope angles at which they are effective can vary markedly with altitude. Thompson (1962), like Daly (1912), has argued the case for control of the alpine accordance levels by regional timberline. Timber cover is seen to maintain lower valley sides at steep angles. Above timberline, alpine processes of avalanching, solifluction, freeze-thaw and nivation are described as cutting into the landscape rapidly, and extending alpine shoulders of relatively low angle from the local"base level" of dense timber. Thompson believes that for the Cascades and Coast Mountains of British

28

Columbia the migration of timberline has been insufficient to
materially affect the argument (c.f. Brink, 1959). He also considers that glaciation has not been a major factor in the alpine and
summit accordances. However, he is dealing with a situation
common to many recently deglaciated mountains. The combination
of jagged, accordant peaks and aretes, low-angle alpine slopes,
and steep-walled valley troughs occurs widely even in mountains
where timberline is hardly a factor. The recently deglaciated
parts of the semi-arid Himalaya afford examples. There is fairly
good evidence that the forms described above will develop through
control of high ice levels rather than timberline. Further, the
enormous variability in timberline where there is not a distinct
glacial trough, suggests that the regular location of that line is a
function of morphology and not vice versa. Thompson describes
graphically how timberline is held back by avalanching and by
debris carried across what are essentially slopes of transportation
in the alpine zone. The difference between invoking glacial as
opposed to timberline control means in many cases that temporal
rather than purely spatial origin of accordance is implied. The
vigour of processes in the alpine zone and their ability to cut and
extend low-angle shoulders need not be in doubt. Troll (1943-44)
has documented the great power of freeze-thaw in alpine regolith,
while Thompson (op. cit.), Veyret (1959) or Gardner and Owens
in this volume, describe vigorous mass movements above timberline. In many areas, however, these processes occur on slopes
which are continuous with the concave or straight profiles of valley
sides. Glaciation or timberline has been offered as means whereby
the alpine processes can have some measure of independent development. Wahrhaftig (1965) has even attacked this kind of thinking as
being unnecessary to explain stepped topography in the Sierra
Nevada.

Another way in which contemporaneous development of
erosion surfaces at different levels can occur has been described
for the Andes and Central Asian mountains. The basic mechanism
was originally proposed by von Richtofen for the mountains of
western China (c.f. Hewitt, 1967, p. 300), and more recently has
been elaborated by Garner (1965). The thesis is that contemporary
rivers in orogenic regions of recent massive uplift may link areas
whose recent erosional development was partially or completely
separate. The separation may have involved climatic, tectonic,
and especially, hydrographic independence. In varying degrees,
the separation of different segments of drainage basins in active
orogenic zones may apply to many less spectacular examples than
the Andes or Central Asian mountains, where basins of interior
drainage seem to have been integrated into the major river systems
only during the Pleistocene. The question of how general landscape
morphology, including accordances, relate to the processes of

drainage integration and development in young orogenic zones has received little attention. Oberlander (1965) has presented a detailed reinterpretation of the matter, and substantially refutes the idea of large-scale superimposition or antecedence of drainage by rivers transverse to orogenic zones. Along with Garner's ideas, this offers an attractive basis for interpreting regional variations in preferred elevations, and hypsometry in terms of the semi-independent development of areas within a gradually integrating drainage system.

In conclusion, we may mention the continuing use of accordances and preferred elevations to deduce tectonic history. It needs stressing in the absence of convincing petrologic or structural data, that accordances are as ambivalent with respect to uplift, as to erosional development. Uplift provides additional relief energy, defining the initial regional slope and location of base level. But neither Walther Penck's notion of slopes formed in accordance with rates of uplift, nor the idea of accordances reflecting the form of uplift can be generally accepted. Drainage development and slope processes in mountain zones may perpetuate the form of uplift but they are equally capable of producing other accordances in geologically very short time spans. This is implied by the various mechanisms described by Daly, Thompson, Garner and Oberlander.

Valley Asymmetry

One of the most convincing areas for demonstrating control of morphology by phyto-climatic conditions is the asymmetry of valley-side slopes (see Hack and Goodlett, 1960; Melton, 1960; Spreizer, 1960; Karrasch, 1970). Asymmetry may arise from structural control over slope processes and selective stream migration. However, it also occurs without, and even in opposition to structural control. In these cases, the asymmetry is often north-south, or related to prevailing wind directions. Work in the Karakoram shows that, if due account is taken of lithological differences, slope angles vary significantly with aspect (Table I).

TABLE I

Mean Slope Angles According to Aspect and
Lithology, Central Karakoram Himalaya
(Hewitt, 1967)

Lithology	Granites			Metamorphics		
Aspect	N	S	All	N	S	All
Angles ($\bar{x}^o$)	58.6	54.8	56.7	46.1	43.5	44.2

30

Melton (1960) suggested that aspectual asymmetry was ultimately a function of the relative power of tributary streams entering main valleys. The more powerful streams undercut and so steepen the opposite valley wall. However, an equally important factor is the rate of sediment production from slopes, since the building outwards of fans and cones will also tend to force the main stream towards the opposite valley wall. In the Central Karakoram the latter seems to reverse Melton's idea. Tributaries from northerly slopes are clearer, larger and persist throughout the summer. But the greater sediment yield from poorly vegetated southerly slopes forces the main rivers against the north-facing slopes.

Characteristic or Threshold Slopes

When traced from mouth to divide of a drainage basin average slope angles tend to lie on a smooth curve and breaks in such curves are usually minor. Yet, it is also observed that the spread of values about the average or modal statistic increases towards the divide, especially when there are mountainous head-waters. The spread of slope angle values, and decreasing smoothness of average curves are positively correlated with average steepness. However, this effect is not always a purely random phenomenon. On the contrary, in landscapes having a significant area of slope greater than about 20°, several modes, or breaks in distribution curves are found and some authors have defined "characteristic slope angles" on this basis (Savigear, 1956).

The interpretation of clustering or breaks in slope angle distributions depends in part upon the scale and detail of sampling. The breaks of slope associated with accordances might produce the effect in coarse sampling. What we are concerned with here are characteristic angles which emerge in careful slope profile analysis or detailed point sampling of slopes. The angles need not be associated with particular altitudinal zones, but a tendency for this to occur is found in the higher mountains.

The weight of contemporary evidence is against the creation of characteristic slopes by erosional processes alone. At the same time Walther Penck's hypothesis noted above has been widely refuted. Erosional processes per se are essentially energy dissipating, order destroying activities which can be expected to produce probabilistic rather than deterministic forms. In particular erosional processes tend to produce a statistical spread of slope angles about a mean which varies solely according to position between divide and base level. The systematic deviation from this pattern and its typically concave upwards, exponential sequence of mean values, may be explained in terms of particular physical constraints upon the processes. In this connection the growing

31

interest of geomorphologists in the properties of materials is very relevant. It offers an explanation in terms of the strength of slope materials, the characteristic slopes being viewed as what Carson describes as "threshold slopes" (1971). Let us take an elementary example. Erosional events of varying magnitude cutting into a slope will, according to their temporal and spatial frequency, produce a statistical spread of angles on the slope. However, if the slope material is close to its critical angle of rest, the whole upper range of erosional events as we have defined them will have the same result, -- to cut the slopes to the critical angle. The distribution of slope angles will be truncated, and a disproportionate number will emerge close to the critical angle for the material. This describes how we might encounter breaks in the distribution of slopes for particular rock-type, vegetation cover and weathering. Clustering of slope angles is less easy to explain. It might occur through a smearing out of the range of freedom in critical slope angle due to inhomogeneities in the strength of slope materials. Alternatively, an uneasy balance between weathering and the rates of supply and removal of debris might produce the same effect.

Earlier, we noted how altitudinal range can produce a series of situations where different threshold slopes become important. The major distinctions among rock materials are between vegetated and unvegetated regolith; between clay-rich and coarse materials; between regolith and solid rock; and between bare rock and snow or ice covered slopes. Climate is important in its influence upon weathering which in turn alters the strength of surface materials; and also by the short-term changes in strength which accompany heat and moisture fluctuations. We expect a threshold slope to represent some balance between these climatic factors and the composition and removal of rock. In regolith, strength depends upon the interlocking and sliding friction of the material. The presence of clays introduces the effect of cohesive forces among the particles, a factor which only tends to be important in high mountains where clays are concentrated in glacial lag deposits. The sensitivity of erosional texture on mountain walls to primary structures, and differences in resistance of rock outcrops is clear. It suggests one mechanism whereby threshold slopes may appear simply due to rock type. In recent years it has been acknowledged that mountain walls and peaks may erode in part due to spontaneous collapse or 'break-out.'' Immediate, or conserved elastic strain due to hydrostatic and tectonic forces may be involved. These will tend to produce planes or other surfaces of concentrated stress which, according to the strength of the rock material, will produce failure surfaces. These may lie at characteristic angles, although it is likely that the surfaces will be curved in many cases and not, therefore, apparent as threshold slopes in the way described earlier. Scheidegger has proposed that the form of cirques, for example, may be more a reflection of stress conditions in the rock salient, than of the mode of flow of the cirque glacier (Scheidegger, 1970, p. 96).

Characteristic slope angles are also found on steep cliffs in perennial snow and ice climates. The angle varies with aspect and seems related primarily to snow and avalanche conditions. According to wind and temperature conditions the snow pack on rock walls will have a certain strength. If slopes are too steep only rime or refrozen meltwater will remain for any length of time, while on gentler slopes, snow will be able to rest and accumulate. If the slopes are moderate, then in an ice climate the snow will develop into a glacier. Between the lower and higher slope values there is a critical zone where snow can be deposited but is close to its limiting angle of repose, and subject to deterioration in strength through diurnal or seasonal modification of the snow pack. Creep in the pack, variations in temperature or the impact of falling snow cornices will cause failure. The successive action of avalanching under these circumstances appears able to maintain avalanche-controlled walls of well-defined average slope. In the Karakoram, perennial snow and ice slopes above 17,000 ft (5100 m) have more than 40% area lying between 55° - 60° and 30% between 56° - 57.5°. Observation of these walls, and their appearance over the past sixty years of expeditions suggest they are maintained by avalanche action. Similar values occur in the summit area of Mt. Rainier in Washington. Perennial snow slopes in the Swiss Alps are said to be rarely greater than 50° (Seligman, 1936, p. 294 and 256), but the data may not refer to avalanche-swept rock walls. It is not clear how avalanche slopes in perennial ice-climates compare with those of only seasonal snow-fall. The action of avalanches in these areas during spring warming, would appear to be important in the formation of chute systems, another feature of mountain rock walls (Matthes, 1938; Markgren, 1964; Hewitt, 1967). Chutes are sometimes a series of sub-parallel grooves, sometimes they follow joints and faults, but in many cases they form high angle drainage networks somewhat reminiscent of those formed by streams. They are usually the rock wall morphological complement of lower talus cones. In the Canadian Rockies it is clear that chutes are places where snow is concentrated, and hence, avalanche activity is considerable. In similar areas of the Himalaya, the author has observed that snow trapped in the chutes may also give rise to debris- and mud-flows of great power. It is not clear what conditions favour the growth of chute networks since they occur in a wide variety of lithologies. Close examination suggests that while Matthes' explanation in terms of avalanching is important, the maintenance of a small flow or drip of moisture in chutes throughout the year must aid in weathering and weakening their floors. However, this moves into the area of detailed process study which is not the concern of this essay. Sufficient to say in conclusion that the most distinctive morphological features of mountains, their areas of bare rock and snow and ice slopes, still remain relatively unknown, though we have some grasp of the main ingredients for interpretation.

CONCLUSION

Studying mountain geomorphology in the present-day context leads to a strong emphasis upon the operation of geomorphic processes. It is an important and necessary development. Mountains are attractive in this regard since the researcher can expect to obtain numerous observations of mass-movement, changes of stream flow and glacial fluctuations in a few field seasons. It is not at all certain that he will have a better sample of this environment than any other, but he will have abundant data from which to build his models. What has been hinted at here is that such work still needs to be related to the larger questions of mountain landscape, either to solve them or restate them in better terms. With material such as is gathered in the present volume, we are in a better position to attempt that task.

SECTION TWO

GLACIAL GEOMORPHOLOGY

Chapter 2-1

PLEISTOCENE CHRONOLOGY AND GEOMORPHOLOGY
OF THE ROCKY MOUNTAINS IN SOUTH AND CENTRAL ALBERTA.

J. Shaw*

Despite relatively intensive study in the major valleys extending eastwards from the Canadian Rocky Mountains there is still no clearly defined glacial chronology for the mountain region. Several of the studies have involved concentrated fieldwork over extensive periods of time, and it might be assumed that deposits and landforms would have been identified and correlated between valleys. However, the various workers have presented evidence for differing numbers of glacial advances within supposedly similar time periods. Consequently, we can either accept that glacial events cannot be correlated between adjacent valleys or that the evidence presented is equivocal. It is worth noting at this stage that dateable material of the radiometric or ash type has provided little useful evidence in the mountain region. The dates obtained have provided only minimum ages for geomorphic events. Critical dates for events within the Wisconsin or Pre-Wisconsin period are not available. The basis of evaluating chronology is almost exclusively stratigraphic evidence. At only one site has an inter-till soil been positively identified and, therefore, the possibilities of confident time correlations are limited. Furthermore unconnected areas of glaciation make continuous tracing of litho-stratigraphic or morphological features impossible. Added complications due to differing glacier responses to climatic changes make for difficulties in establishing regional chronologies. Although it is thought that generally over long periods of time glacier responses will be synchronous, over short periods glacier surges may produce contrasting responses in adjacent valleys. For any one glaciation the effects of surges are, therefore, likely to cause oscillations superimposed on larger period oscillations related to glacier stades and interstades. A more serious problem is introduced by the meso climatic, morphological and lithological controls which may cause differences in the extent of ice advance, in the nature of ice decay, and in the amount of debris and consequent size of moraines, for the same advance phase in adjacent valleys.

---

*The financial support of the National Research Council of Canada is gratefully acknowledged.

In this paper I shall examine the evidence and conclusions presented for glacial chronological and geomorphic studies within the Rocky Mountains and Foothills zones. Finally an attempt will be made to show similarities between areas and by rather indirect methods outline a chronology which must be accepted with reservation.

SOUTHWESTERN ALBERTA

The major work discussing the glacial chronology of the Rocky Mountains and Foothills of Southwestern Alberta is that of Wagner (1966). However, important contributions from Stalker (1963, 1969) and Horberg (1952, 1954) will also be considered in this section. Wagner's work is largely confined to the Castle, Crowsnest, Oldman and Belly Rivers (Figure 1). Although glaciations of mountain provenance show pronounced morainic features, Wagner establishes the glacial history on the basis of stratigraphic units. Eight principal units are identified, basal gravels, lacustrine, eolian and fluviatile sediments, bedrock masses, Mountain till and Laurentide till. Time stratigraphic units comprise two Mountain and three Laurentide tills, basal gravel and an alluvial silt. A two fold major subdivision of the Mountain tills is made. A lower Mountain till is identified in only a few sites and in each

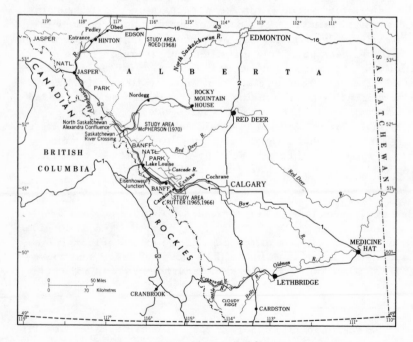

Figure 1 - South Central Alberta

38

case occurs below an upper Mountain till. At one important section (Cloud Ridge, Figure 1) a deep soil which occurs above the lower till provides the evidence used to differentiate between two major glacial events. The extent of the advance of the glacier which deposited the lower till and details of its retreat are undocumented on account of the limited stratigraphic observations and complete absence of morphological expression of the till.

A second major advance is subdivided according to stratigraphic and morphological evidence. The upper tills are generally less than 20 ft (6 m) thick but may exceed 50 ft (15 m) in surface moraines. During the maximum stage of the second major advance the Mountain piedmont glacier and the Continental glacier were contiguous. Abutment of the two ice masses is considered to be illustrated by the intercalatory contacts between the upper Mountain tills and Laruentide tills. With retreat of the Mountain glaciers pro-glacial drainage toward the north-east was blocked by the Laurentide ice and a series of pro-glacial lakes were formed. Minor oscillations in the retreat of the Mountain glaciers are inferred from the interfingering nature of the tills and lacustrine deposits. However, the possibility of till flowage (Hartshorn, 1958) casts doubt on the necessity of oscillations. Stillstands or even minor advances are inferred from two sets of moraines. The outer moraines (Foothills moraines of Wagner) are in reality tracts of hummocky moraine up to 4 mi (6.5 km) in width. The inner moraines occur behind the mountain front and are clearly developed in the Oldman, West Castle and Crowsnest river valleys. The inner moraines show clear ridge forms which may indicate a steep, active ice front possibly associated with an ice advance phase. Each of the inner moraines is related to a stream terrace in their respective valleys which graded into a lake at an elevation of 3900 ft (1185 m) (Lake Cardston). The relatively temporary nature of lake levels in this area Horberg (1954), leads to the conclusion that any geomorphic features closely related to a single lake level are likely of contemporaneous formation. Therefore, in southwestern Alberta at least we may correlate morainic features between valleys.

The morphological evidence indicates that ice stagnation was an important feature in the process of glacial retreat of the Mountain glaciers. Evidence from glacial erratics of Mountain provenance may be used to infer maximum ice thickness of something less than 2000 ft (600 m) in the foothills.

In several instances Mountain glacial episodes have been tentatively correlated with Continental sequences. Wagner (1966) showed that the lower Mountain till is older than the first

Continental ice event. Stalker (1963) has established the first
continental event to be earlier than 37,000 B.P. The thick soil
above this till suggests a Pre-Wisconsin date for the lower
Mountain till and Wagner has tentatively correlated this till with
the Illinoian. Wagner (1966) states that the moraines of the upper
Mountain till "all show shallow depths of leaching (generally less
than 2 ft (0.6 m)), mostly unweathered surface stones, poor
drainage integration, and bold morainic form all of which indicate
a Late Wisconsin age." By rather tenuous extrapolation Wagner
considers the retreat phases of the second Mountain glacial advance
to be confined to the early and mid-Pinedale stades of the Cordilleran
chronology outlined by Richmond (1965). However, Stalker (1967)
has suggested that terminal moraines which occur further down-
valley of both the inner and Foothills moraines of Wagner (1966)
are of Late Pinedale age. In both cases the chronological deduc-
tions are based on inconclusive evidence. The stratigraphic
relationship between samples taken for radiometric dating and the
terminal moraine identified by Stalker (1969) permits a much older
deposition of the moraine than Stalker suggests. Wagner (1966)
states that his correlations are on a "finger-matching basis" and
should be taken as such.

BOW VALLEY

The major work carried out to elucidate Quaternary
events in the mountain reaches of the Bow Valley is that of Rutter
(1965, 1966). Rutter's arguments are based principally on geomorphic and stratigraphic observations. Some relationship is to
be expected between events outlined by Rutter and the series of
terraces described by Stalker (1968) in the Cochrane area
(Figure 1) which lies downvalley of Rutter's field area. Stalker
has obtained a date for one terrace and this may provide a possible
time marker for the mountain events.

The lowest and oldest Quaternary sediment recognised
by Rutter is a stratified gravel which occurs below the lowest till
in the region. Although there is no evidence of cold conditions at
the time of deposition of these gravels Rutter (1966) chooses to
identify them with a glacial event which he calls the Pre-Bow
Valley Advance. Stream diversion to the south of Banff townsite
is considered to have taken place during the retreat phase of this
ice mass. The later advances to be described are probably of
Wisconsin age and, therefore, it is highly likely that the Bow
Valley was glaciated several times prior to the Wisconsin.
However, it seems unnecessary to equate the gravels and the
diversion with any single advance.

The first clear evidence of glacial advance in the Bow Valley is a widespread glacial till which covers much of the valley floor southeast of Eisenhower Junction (Figure 1). The till covers the gravels discussed above, and its deposition is believed to be contemporaneous with the formation of ice marginal stream channels which show as linear breaks on the valley side slopes. Maximum elevation of the marginal channels occurs at 8200 ft (2490 m). There is no terminal moraine associated with this advance, but Rutter (1966) suggested that pauses in ice retreat are represented by ice contact stratified drift at Canmore and the junction of the Bow and Cascade Rivers near Banff (Figure 1).

Rutter (1966) proposes a readvance of the Bow Valley Advance glacier on the basis of stratigraphic and morphological evidence. Ice marginal channels at 5300 ft (1610 m) and a thin, surficial till overlying outwash related to the Bow Valley Advance glacier provide the main evidence presented to support the Bow Valley Readvance proposal. Stagnant ice moraine which occurs east of Exshaw is related to the Bow Valley readvance and, therefore, this advance is considered to have extended across previously deposited end-moraines of the Bow Valley Advance which occur upvalley from Exshaw at Canmore and near to the Bow-Cascade confluence. The evidence presented above for the Bow Valley readvance is a good example of the equivocal nature of the stratigraphic and geomorphic observations. Rutter presents no evidence to suggest that the Exshaw moraine is younger than the Canmore or Bow-Cascade moraines. In the light of glacier thinning during retreat (Flint, 1957) the evidence of ice marginal channels at levels lower than the maximum altitude may equally well be related to stillstand during a single advance as to readvance. Furthermore observations at modern ice fronts illustrate that multiple tills may occur associated with a single retreat and that till overlying outwash does not necessarily imply ice advance (Boulton, 1968).

Prominent lateral moraines and related ice marginal terraces in the Valley of Ten Peaks, Consolation Valley and the main Bow Valley are related to a further readvance, the Eisenhower Junction Advance, which is represented by a terminal moraine of ice stratified drift near Eisenhower Junction (Rutter, 1966). A significantly longer period since deglaciation for areas downvalley from the Eisenhower Junction moraine than those areas upstream is inferred from the greater development of alluvial fans in down-valley locations. Rutter (1966) also proposed a readvance across the Eisenhower Advance terminal moraine. The evidence for this readvance is based on a thin till overlying the stratified materials of the terminal moraine and also the presence of ice marginal features at a lower level than the Eisenhower Advance features.

Again thin till overlying stratified material does not imply glacial readvance, and furthermore it is difficult to imagine that a thin glacier could advance further down valley than an earlier thicker one.

Rutter (1965) has correlated the Bow Valley Advance, the Bow Valley Readvance and the Eisenhower Junction Advance with the three stades of the Pinedale, (Richmond, 1965). A date from the North Saskatchewan Valley of 9330 ± 170 C^{14} years B.P. is considered by Rutter to provide a minimum age for the Eisenhower Junction Advance. This would put the Eisenhower Junction Advance in the very early part of the Late Pinedale stade and would imply ice advance during a Pinedale interstadial. Evidently either age interpretations of Rutter (1966) or Richmond (1965) are erroneous or alternatively the sequence of events in the Bow Valley and in the Rocky Mountains of the United States are discrepant. Stalker (1968) has illustrated that aggradation in the Bow Valley took place about 11,000 years B.P. and culminated in the formation of a floodplain some 70 ft (21 m) above the present river level. Observations by Stalker are limited to one locality in the foothills near Cochrane and this terrace has not been traced up or down valley. Stalker (1968) considers the aggradation to have occurred during a glacial advance down the Bow Valley. Wagner's work to the south has established a relationship between morainic features and terraces. Similar relationships between Pinedale moraines and river terraces are reported from Wyoming, (Moss and Bonini, 1961). In the absence of dateable material in the upper reaches of the Bow Valley, correlation of the aggradational terrace near Cochrane with the stratigraphy and morainic sequence identified by Rutter could provide a useful reference for what is at present a highly confused chronology.

THE NORTH SASKATCHEWAN VALLEY

The major work in the Upper Saskatchewan Valley is that of McPherson (1970) who confined attention to the section of the valley within the Main and Front Ranges of the Mountains. Drill records from the Big Horn Dam site reveal 120 to 130 ft (36 to 39 m) of gravel resting on a till which overlies bedrock. The till is associated with an ice advance, the Big Horn advance, (McPherson, 1970). Subsequent to this advance stream aggradation was responsible for the deposition of at least 350 ft (105 m) of sands and gravels. A second major advance, the Main glacial advance, was responsible for the deposition of large quantities of till and the creation of the present day glacial landforms. Deglaciation of the Main advance glacier was by both back wasting and by ice stagnation, each process having been dominant at different times. Two minor readvance phases or stillstands in the recession

42

of the Main advance glacier are inferred from end moraines at Saskatchewan Crossing and at the junction of the North Saskatchewan and Alexandra rivers, (Figure 1). A C^{14} date obtained from charcoal near the base of loess overlying fluvio-glacial sands and gravels indicates that the valley close to Saskatchewan Crossing was ice free 9330 ± 170 C^{14} years B.P.,(Westgate and Dreimanis, 1967). Stream degradation of 18 ft (5.4 m) has occurred in the last 9000 years.

The terminal position of the Main advance has not been identified. Ice thicknesses in excess of 2000 ft (600 m) are postulated for the valley downstream of Saskatchewan Crossing.

THE ATHABASCA VALLEY

The Athabasca valley glacial sequence has been studied by Roed (1968). Roed's study was carried out in the Hinton-Edson area where considerable interaction between the Laurentide and Cordilleran ice masses is recognised. A good deal of Roed's work is devoted to identification of till formations and the application of lithostratigraphic techniques to the problem of glacial chronology. There is much similarity in the approach of Roed and that of Wagner (1966). As in south-western Alberta the oldest surficial deposit in the Athabasca Valley is a basal gravel which does not contain erratics from the Canadian Shield. These gravels are variously sub-divided according to their position relative to bedrock terraces and buried valleys. However, as pointed out by Wagner (1966) the gravel sub-divisions are not distinguishable on the basis of lithology.

Tills form the most widespread glacial deposit in the Hinton-Edson area and on the basis of lithostratigraphy Roed has differentiated four Cordilleran or Mountain tills. Furthermore, Cordilleran erratics at high altitude several miles to the east of limits associated with the above tills suggests an earlier advance from the mountains which predates the till deposition. The presence of seemingly anomalous drainage patterns and the limited distribution of erratics from the earliest known Laurentide advance are also used to infer an early Cordilleran advance. The oldest Cordilleran till, the Marlboro till, may overlie bedrock or the preglacial gravels. An abrupt lateral contact is shown between the Marlboro till and the Edson till, of Laurentide origin. Consequently at the time of deposition of the Marlboro till the Cordilleran and Laurentide glaciers were contiguous. The orientation of drumlins in the area clearly indicates the deflection of flowlines which occurred as a result of interference between the Cordilleran and Laurentide ice masses (Roed, 1968). A rather interesting feature of the interaction of the two ice masses is the development of two erratic trains associated with the Marlboro till, (Roed, et al, 1967). The Athabasca Valley erratics train consists of metamorphic material from west of the continental divide which was confined to ice diverted northwards by the Laurentide ice mass. Consequently this material is not found south of Hinton. However, quartzitic rocks believed to have been derived from the Jasper area were carried in ice deflected south-wards and deposited in a narrow linear belt along the Foothills of Alberta and into Montana, (Stalker, 1956). The Marlboro till is associated with broad bands of end-moraine which consist of a series of lobate ridges interspersed with areas of hummocky dead ice moraine. Drumlins and flutings are also associated with the Marlboro till. The retreat of the Marlboro till from a common position with the Laurentide till was accompanied by the development of glacier dammed lakes into which a rather varied lithologic unit, the Pedley sediments, (Roed, 1968), was deposited. Lithologic variety may simply represent changing facies of a proglacial situation. A proglacial situation is favoured by the presence of till interbeds within the Pedley sediments. It would appear that the Pedley sediments are interstadial, although Roed does consider the possibility of interglacial rank.

Subsequent to the Marlboro advance a further advance from the mountains is established on stratigraphic and morpho-logical grounds. A till overlying the Pedley sediments is associated with drumlins and end-moraine features which truncate drumlins and end-moraines of the Marlboro advance. This upper till is named the Obed till, and is only distinguishable from the Marlboro till when separated by interstadial sediments. Two main pauses in the recession of the Obed glacier are associated with kame complexes and with the development of two distinct stream terrace levels. The upper terrace level has an average height of 190 ft (57 m) above the Athabasca river and is associated with prominent ice terminus deposits near Entrance (Figure 1). Further retreat of the glacier was accompanied by degradation of the river and the formation of a second terrace or terrace complex, with local relief of up to 50 ft (15 m), (Stene, 1966). The position of the ice terminus during the formation of the lower terrace complex is unknown.

DISCUSSION

A certain degree of agreement between the areas considered can be seen in terms of a general picture. In each case a major advance responsible for most of the present day glacigenic deposits and landforms is postulated. In south-western Alberta, and in the Athabasca Valley this advance is shown to be

contiguous with Laurentide ice, (Wagner, 1966 , Roed, 1968).
Contact between the two ice masses for the North Saskatchewan
or Bow Valleys has not been proven. Tentatively we could suggest
that the above advances in each valley represent similar time
periods. This may then be used as a stratigraphic datum for
comparing other events (Table I). Table I illustrates that evidence
for an advance older than the major advance is seen in each area.
However, only Wagner (1966) and McPherson (1970) confidently
identify tills of this advance. However, it is felt that the agreement
in terms of the older advance represents generally synchronous
major events in each area. Confusion arises in the more detailed
interpretations of the events post-dating the major advance.
McPherson (1970) and Wagner (1966) consider a relatively constant ice recession from this advance with only minor oscillations
occurring. Rutter (1965, 1966) and Roed (1968) suggest a major
readvance occurring subsequent to the major advance. Explanation
of these differences cannot be assigned to latitudinal effects as they
occur in alternate valleys. It may be that evidence is better preserved in the Athabasca and Bow Valleys permitting more intricate
reconstructions. Alternatively glacier behaviour as outlined in the
introduction may have been different in each valley. Finally it is
always possible that misinterpretation of deposits and morphological
features has caused single advances to be recognised as multiple
glaciations or vice versa. In view of the confusion within the area
it is presumptious to attempt correlation with either the chronology
presented by Richmond (1965) for the Rocky Mountains in the
United States or with the chronologies presented for the Plains
region. Until more informative dates or better relative age
criteria are applied within the area the present confusion will
remain.

TABLE I

South-western Alberta (Wagner, 1966 Stalker, 1963)	Bow Valley (Rutter, 1965,66; Stalker, 1968)	North Saskatchewan Valley (McPherson, 1970)	Athabasca Valley (Stene, 1966; Roed, et al., 1967 . Roed, 1968)
	Eisenhower Junction Readvance		Lower Valley Train
Mountain Front Moraines	Eisenhower Junction Advance	Alexandra Moraine	Upper Valley Train Entrance Moraine
Foothills Moraines	Bow Valley Readvance	Saskatchewan Bridge Moraine	Obed Advance
Upper Mountain Till (M 11)	Bow Valley Advance	Main Glacial Advance	Marlboro Advance
Cloudy Ridge Soil			
Lower Mountain Till (M 1)	Pre-Bow Valley Advance	Big Horn Advance	Unnamed (evidence from erratics)

Chapter 2-2

GLACIAL HISTORY OF THE BOW RIVER AND RED DEER RIVER AREAS AND THE ADJACENT FOOTHILLS.

Stuart A. Harris and A. N. Boydell

The area south of Bow Summit in Banff National Park is probably one of the most frequently studied areas in Western Canada as regards its glacial history (see Rutter, 1972). Recently, a considerable amount of work has been carried out in the Rocky Mountain Foothills, and in the following account, an attempt will be made to summarize on-going research on glacial and post-glacial history in the Foothills zone.

STUDY AREA

Figure 1 shows the major valleys and settlements discussed in this chapter. The Rocky Mountains consist of a series of thrust blocks pushed eastwards towards the Prairies. The bedrock strikes NNW-SSE and both the drainage and the former

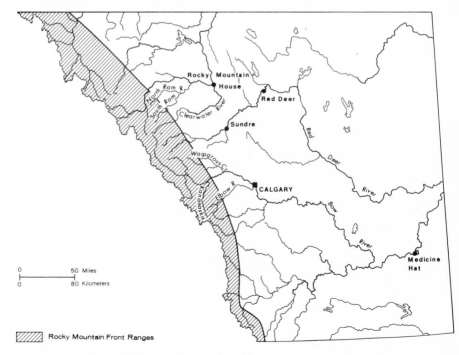

Figure 1 - Location Map

mountain ice had to cross the strike ridges. The Continental Divide lies well above the level of the valleys to the west and Cordilleran ice failed to penetrate the region. Thus only the local Rocky Mountain tills (dominated by limestones, dolomites, quartzites, and black cherts) and Laurentide till (characterized by granite and high grade metamorphic pebbles) are found in the area.

Each valley appears to have had a different history of Late glacial ice advance. On the other hand the last Laurentide advance can be traced from the Edson-Hinton area through to Priddis, south of Calgary. Because it was so widespread, it forms a reference plane from which we can deduce the relative ages of the events in many of the other valleys.

THE LAURENTIDE ADVANCES

The evidence for the number of Laurentide advances varies from area to area. Roed (1968) recognized two advances in the Edson-Hinton area, while Boydell (1970) was only able to find evidence of one till near Sundre.

The last major Laurentide ice sheet advanced from the north past Edmonton, Sundre and Calgary (Figure 2) between 25,000 and 14,000 years ago (Westgate, pers. comm., 1971). It

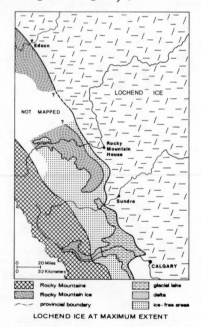

LOCHEND ICE AT MAXIMUM EXTENT

Figure 2 - Limits of Lochend Ice

48

blocked the drainage from the mountains producing proglacial lakes e.g., in the Bow Valley. The outlet of this lake was at 4300 ft (1300 m) into the Priddis area from the Elbow river valley (Seagal, 1971). Glacier Peak ash (age c. 12,700 years B.P.) appears to have been found in the lake deposits near Cochrane, thus suggesting an age for this lake. When the supply of ice ceased, melting in the zone northeast of Edmonton produced kettle lakes by 11,400 $\pm$ 190 years B.P. (GSC-10491 Lichti-Federovich, 1970). There could have been a draining of the lake at Calgary about this time since river gravels containing western pebbles and bones of this age occur at Cochrane (Stalker, 1968).

The ice persisted rather longer in the Rocky Mountain House-Calgary area, since the Bow and Red Deer valleys again became blocked. A C^{14} date from proglacial lake Sundre, corresponding to its lowest spillway came out at 10,700 $\pm$ 150 years B.P. (I-5126), while the date for shell in the Lake Calgary deposits at lower elevations near Cochrane was 9,650 $\pm$ 160 years B.P. (I5676).

Near Rocky Mountain House, ice stagnation had taken place so that on the surface of the ice lakes were formed in which mollusca flourished. Round the edges of the lakes bison roamed. A C^{14} date on the bison is dated at 9,670 $\pm$ 140 years B.P. (I-5677), while on the shell the date is 10,250 $\pm$ year B.P. (I-5675).

Tills recognized by various authors that are thought to correspond to this general ice advance are the Lochend and Balzac tills of Tharin (1960), which appear to be a single till, which we shall call the Lochend till, the "Laurentide till" of Boydell (1970) and Seagal (1971), and the Edson and Mayberne tills and Mixed till of Roed (1968). Only in the Edson-Hinton and Rocky Mountain House areas did the Laurentide ice actually coalesce with mountain ice. Roed also recognized an earlier Laurentide till, the Marsh Creek till, at a single locality. At another locality north of Cochrane, an earlier Laurentide till is also found. Thus the Lochend ice was not the only major incursion of Continental ice into the area.

MOUNTAIN ICE ADVANCES

At some time during the Wisconsin period, ice flowed down all the river valleys draining the eastern side of the mountains. However, the sequence and area affected varies from valley to valley so that there is little evidence to support the concept of correlation by height of ice in terminal moraines (Richmond, 1965). In small valleys such as Waiparous Creek, the ice only

49

just reached the Foothills, whereas some of the larger valleys
produced glaciers that spread out on to the plain as huge piedmont
lobes. Accordingly we will discuss the evidence from each major
valley that has been examined so far.

The Bow River

This is one of the largest rivers in the area and has its
source beside the Continental Divide. Four ice advances have been
recognized so far (Rutter, 1972). The earliest left a black till at a
series of localities along the Bow river in the Foothills region.
Its age is unknown and its source is presumed to be in the Bow
Valley.

Some time later came a major ice incursion called the
Bow Valley Advance by Rutter (1972). Somewhere in the Calgary
area is its eastward margin, while it also flowed northwards as
far as the Waiparous Creek Campground. The distance it spread
southward is presently unknown but major diffluence of ice took
place below Banff with Bow ice spreading southwards over the
lower cols into the lower Kananaskis valley and into the headwaters
of the Jumping Pound Creek and Elbow river valley (Walker, 1971).
The ice thickness at this time was between 1600 and 2600 ft in the
main mountain valley (Rutter, 1972).

The ice retreated beyond Canmore and then readvanced
as the Canmore Advance to the mouth of the Kananaskis valley.
In front of the ice, a delta was built into Lake Calgary past Morley
village. Then the ice retreated up valley to make one last minor
advance (the Eisenhower Junction Advance) which reached as far
as Eisenhower Junction. Thereafter, the only evidence of
increased glacial action is during the Neoglacial period.

The Spy Hill till thought to be part of the main Bow
Valley Advance, occurs in places, below the Lochend till and
above the older Laurentide till, and a re-examination shows that
Spy Hill till overlies the upper two terraces of Stalker (1968) at
Cochrane. The lower terraces are cut in mountain outwash
gravels containing bones of Bighorn sheep, the extinct Western
Bison, the extinct Mexican Ass, Wapati and Caribou (Churcher,
1968). C^{14} dates on the bones range from $10,760 \pm 160$ years
B.P. (GSC-612) to $11,370 \pm 170$ years B.P. (GSC-613), i.e.,
these deposits were probably deposited during the period in which
Lake Calgary was dry in the middle of the Lochend ice advance.

Rutter (1972) regards the Eisenhower Junction Advance
as being earlier than $9,330 \pm 170$ years B.P. (GSC-332).
Unfortunately this date comes from another valley and there is no

direct evidence from south of Bow Summit. Accepting his correlation, the sequence of events appears as in Figure 3. It shows a pattern of rapid readvances similar to those seen in

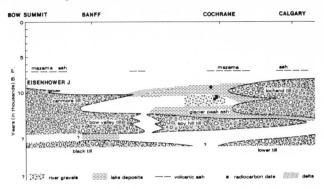

Figure 3 - Suggested relationship between tills and other deposits in the Bow Valley.

Southern Saskatchewan (Christiansen, 1965) and in Eastern North America (Goldthwaite et al, 1965) rather than the sequence suggested by Richmond (1965, 1970).

Red Deer Valley

In this valley, evidence for only one mountain ice advance has been described (Pheasant, 1968; Boydell, 1970). The ice immediately preceeded the arrival of the Laurentide ice in the Sundre area so that the advance appears to be equivalent to the Spy Hill till in age and it spread out as a piedmont lobe which flowed southeastwards, almost reaching Cochrane. It may have coalesced with Bow Valley ice in the south, but it had retreated before Lake Sundre was formed. A C^{14} date was obtained by M. J. Chambers on shell in basal alluvium over the till at latitude 51° 42'30" N, by longitude 115° 39'30" N within Banff Park of 11,220 ± 680 years B.P. (WSU-881). Retreat was much more rapid in this valley.

Locally between the Red Deer and Bow rivers, there exists a zone which contains no glacial erratics. This is currently being examined in order to check up on whether ice ever crossed it, but it seems probable that it may be a zone unglaciated during at least the Wisconsin period. Similar areas have also been located between some of the major river valleys to the north. Smaller valleys such as the Waiparous Creek had only minor glaciers in them that scarcely reached the foot of the Rocky Mountains.

Foothills Valley to the North

North of the Red Deer river, Boydell has examined the valleys of the Clearwater, Ram and North Saskatchewan Rivers. Only a single till occurs in the Clearwater valley which only just reaches beyond the easternmost margin of the Brazeau Range.

The Ram river has two branches -- the North and South Ram rivers. Glacial deposits are absent in the North Ram valley whereas in the South Ram river valley, deposits of three glacial advances occur. The oldest till (Hummingbird till) is cemented and a gorge has been cut in it. Below the gorge, uncemented deltaic sands and gravels, correlated with about 20m(65 ft) of titled varves further downstream represent the second glacial episode. These are separated by an erosional haitus from the tills and gravels of the youngest advance. The latter appears to be the same age as the Spy Hill event in the Bow, Red Deer and Clearwater valleys. Yet a fourth till exists on the 4000 ft (1200 m) plateau surface to the east of the Brazeau Range between the Clearwater and Ram rivers. It is deeply dissected and highly weathered. Since it is absent from the valleys cut into the surface, it may be pre-Wisconsin in age.

The next major river flowing through the Foothills is the North Saskatchewan river, which exhibits three tills between Nordegg and Rocky Mountain House. Two are Rocky Mountain tills, and the third, the "Mixed till" (Roed, 1968) is interpreted as being Laurentide (Lochend) till. The two mountain tills are found in superposition along the river, but the younger till (probably equiva- lent to the Lochend/Spy Hill event) is the more extensive. The mixed till is found in the vicinity of Rocky Mountain House, and grades eastward into typical Laurentide till. In the Sundre area, this mixed till can no longer be distinguished from the Laurentide, which also becomes the principal deposit associated with the Foot- hills Erratics Train -- a train of felspathic sandstones and arkoses stretching from Edson to North Dakota (Stalker, 1956). It is concluded that its mixed characteristics are the result of incorporation of earlier Cordilleran deposits by the advancing Laurentide ice in the Athabasca valley area.

POST-GLACIAL CLIMATIC CHANGES

Examining the mollusca from the proglacial and supra- glacial lake sediments and from post-glacial alluvium, it is possible to derive some indication of past climatic conditions (Harris and Pip, 1972). These can be compared with the very limited data from pollen studies (Lichti-Fedorovich, 1971).

The climate was already warming when the Lochend ice was at its maximum. Southern warm water mollusca were living in the major lakes alongside the ice sheet although colonization of all kettle holes took much longer and may still be incomplete. Poplar colonized the first patches of land between the stagnating ice sheets but was soon followed by evergreen forest, which covered the Prairies. Precipitation gradually decreased as temperatures rose to the Altithermal. The mountain glaciers responded much faster than the Laurentide ice because of the higher rates of precipitation and ablation or melting at lower latitudes.

Altithermal conditions lasted from approximately 9500 - 6000 years B.P., or until just after the deposition of the Mazama ash. The forests gradually disappeared from the main Prairie zone as precipitation decreased, but the water balance was always more favourable to plant growth than at present, as shown by the forest-grassland boundaries. After 6000 years B.P., the climate became cooler and drier and since 3500 years B.P. has been roughly the same as at present, although with some minor fluctuations.

Chapter 2-3

RECENT GLACIAL ACTIVITY AND SOME ASSOCIATED LANDFORMS IN THE CANADIAN ROCKY MOUNTAINS.

James Gardner

Glaciers of various sizes and types are present in the Canadian Rocky Mountains. They are remnants of the Neoglaciation, a period comprising the last 400 to 500 years (Heusser, 1956; Porter and Denton, 1967). Of particular interest in this paper is the last century, during which the glaciers have receded from near their Neoglacial maxima. The record of glacial activity should be instructive for the geomorphologist in that the recession has produced, or revealed, a variety of landforms some of which are described in the paper. In addition, the paper briefly describes the present extent and character of glaciation in the area.

The area of primary interest is the central portion of the Canadian Rockies. Extending 300 km (180 mi) between Lake Louise and Mt. Robson, the central region is the most heavily glaciated part of the range (Figure 1). The mountains may be divided into the Main Ranges and the Front Ranges. The former are made up of near horizontal beds of Cambrian and older quartzitic sandstones, limestones, dolomites and shales. The Front Ranges are composed of Devonian and younger limestones, dolomites and shales which dip steeply to the west. Mt. Robson (4000 m, 12, 972 ft.) is the highest point in the Canadian Rockies. The majority of the peaks in the Main Ranges vary between 3125 m (10, 000 ft.) and 3600 m (11, 500 ft.) while those in the Front Ranges vary between 2800 m (9000 ft.) and 3280 m (10, 500 ft.). Local relief is generally in the order of 1400 m (4100 ft.) to 1900 m (6000 ft.). Although the Main Ranges along the continental divide are the most heavily glaciated today, the general physiography testifies to intensive and extensive past glaciations.

THE DATA SOURCES

An historical record, constructed from a variety of data sources, exists for glacial activity over the last 100 years. Descriptions of Rocky Mountain glaciers date from the time when Athabasca Pass was a major fur-trade thoroughfare. Scott Glacier, near Athabasca Pass, received attention from David Douglas in 1827 (Douglas, 1914) and, as exploration proceeded further south, other glaciers were described. The Lyell and Freshfield glaciers intrigued James Hector of the Palliser Expedition to the extent that he left detailed descriptions of them in 1858 and 1859. Thorington (1927) used these descriptions to establish datums from which to measure frontal recession. Dawson's 1884 photograph of the Drummond glacier was used in a similar fashion by Nelson et al (1966).

By the 1890's much of the exploration was of a recreational nature. Mountaineer-explorers such as W. D. Wilcox, C. E. Fay, J. Habel and C. S. Thompson left a rich legacy of photographs and descriptions of the Bow, **Peyto, Alexandra,** Victoria and Yoho glaciers.

The study of glaciers for their own sake began in the early part of the twentieth century (see for example: Sherzer, 1907; Vaux, 1909; Coleman 1912). With the inauguration of the Alpine Club of Canada in 1906 systematic studies of several glaciers over a period of years began (see for example: Wheeler, 1931, 1933). With the influx of tourists in the early part of this century and with the extensive operations of the Interprovincial Boundary Survey and the Topographic Survey, a vast photographic record of glaciers accumulated.[1]

Since the 1940's, the study of glaciers in the Canadian Rockies has increasingly fallen to professional glaciologists and water resource researchers. Agencies of the federal government have carried out long-term studies of recession and discharge (Davies, 1964; Campbell et al,1969a and b). Additional data have been gathered on glacier mass budgets and volumetric changes particularly on the Peyto and Ram River glaciers (Ostrem, 1966. and Henoch, 1971). Independent researchers have studied the flow, surface velocity and seismicity of the Saskatchewan and Athabasca glaciers (see for example: Meier, 1960; Paterson, 1964; Neave and Savage, 1969; Paterson, 1970; Raymond, 1971). Interest in long-term glacier fluctuations has continued (Field, 1949; Heusser, 1956; Nelson et al, 1966; Brunger et al, 1967).

Despite the long history of formal and informal glacier study, data for the whole range is sporadic. This is especially true for the regions south of Banff and north of Mt. Robson, and in the Front Ranges generally. Research has been complicated by the vast area, the relative inaccessibility and restrictions on certain

---

[1]Notable collections of these photographs may be found in the Archives of the Canadian Rockies, Banff; The Department of Geography, University of Calgary; American Geographical Society, New York; Royal Geographical Society, London.

modes of transportation.

THE PRESENT EXTENT OF GLACIATION

A glacier map of southern British Columbia and Alberta
is the most recent attempt to portray the extent of glaciation
(Falconer, et al, 1966). As with any glacier inventory based
primarily on interpretation of air photographs, this is fraught with
the usual problems of defining glacier margins when a persistent
seasonal snow cover or a heavy debris cover is present.

In the heavily glaciated central portion of the Canadian
Rockies several large (50 to 150 km^2; 20 to 60 mi^2) icefields are
present. The Columbia Icefield is the largest and most notable for
the number of important distributary glaciers to which it gives rise.
Other important icefields include: Wapta, Chaba, and Lyell. It is
estimated that the extent of glaciation in the North Saskatchewan
Basin, which includes part of the Columbia Icefield and the Lyell
Icefield, has decreased by 10% since 1948 (Henoch, 1971).

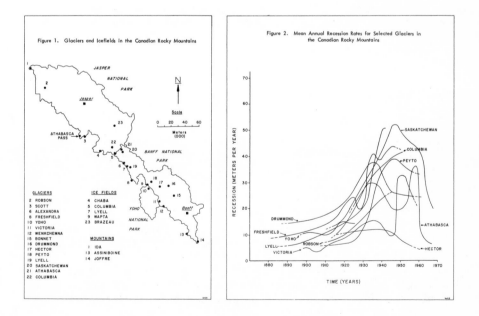

Outside the Main Ranges in the central region, the only glacial features of icefield dimensions and morphology are in the Mt. Ida area north of Mt. Robson, at the head of the Brazeau River (Brazeau Icefield) and in the vicinity of Mt. Joffre in the French military group (Figure 1). Other notable glaciated areas are in the vicinities of Mts. Assiniboine and Sir Douglas south of Banff and in the Drummond and Bonnet areas of the Front Ranges. Otherwise, the glaciated area of the Canadian Rockies is made up of numerous cirque and small valley glaciers scattered throughout.

In the vertical dimension, the present glaciation limits in the Canadian Rocky Mountains vary between 2600 and 3100 m (8500 ft and 10,200 ft) (Ostrem, 1966a). The limit is lowest in the western portions of the Main Range and increases in an easterly direction into the Front Ranges. The glaciation limit is the critical height that must be exceeded by the land surface before glaciers will form. It is to be distinguished from the climatic snowline and the equilibrium line which have been placed at 2400 m (8000 ft) and above in this region (Meier and Post, 1962).

THE TYPES OF GLACIERS

The glaciers of the Canadian Rocky Mountains take several forms, including: icefields, valley glaciers of the outlet type, valley glaciers of the Alpine type (Embleton and King, 1968), cirque glaciers and cliff or niche glaciers (Groom, 1959). Icefields are few in number with the result that valley glaciers of the outlet type are also few. The Columbia Icefield is the best example of the former while the Saskatchewan, Athabasca and Columbia Glaciers are the best examples of the latter. Valley glaciers of the Alpine type are more numerous with the Robson and Freshfield glaciers being the largest and best examples. Cirque glaciers are the most ubiquitous form in the region. In the Main Range cliff or niche glaciers are common.

Set apart by their high debris content or cover are ice accumulations variously referred to as ice-cored moraines (Ostrem & Arnold, 1970), rock glaciers or simply debris-covered glaciers. These features are common in the Front Ranges and the southern parts of the Main Range. Perhaps the most spectacular example is the Wenkchemna glacier in the Lake Louise district. The recent behavior of this type of ice body has been distinct from that of other glaciers and a unique set of depositional landforms is resulting from the stagnating ice.

THE RECENT GLACIAL ACTIVITY

A major portion of the glacial data from the Canadian Rocky Mountains is simply a record of frontal recession. This recession has been general for the last seventy years and perhaps since the Neoglaciation maximum. The recession has not taken place at a constant rate however, nor has it been uniform between glaciers. In a survey paper, Meier and Post (1962) calculated that, of the glaciers in this region, 52% were retreating, 43% were "active," 5% were stagnant and none were advancing. The most comprehensive of published surveys (Field and Heusser, 1954) confirms the general recession.

Data for several selected glaciers are presented in Table I and recession rates for the last one hundred years are portrayed in Figure 2. The data indicate that the recession proceeded slowly and regularly until about 1920 after which it accelerated to a maximum in the period 1945 to 1955. Where frequent data are available for a number of years, such as for the Freshfield glacier between 1924 and 1945, it can be seen that recession rates fluctuated greatly from one year to the next. Since the period of maximum recession there has been a general decline in the rate, an observation that has been especially evident on the Saskatchewan and Athabasca glaciers (Figure 2).

The glacier recession and its fluctuating rates have been explained in terms of climatic change (Heusser, 1956; Brunger et al, 1967; Henoch, 1971). The marked recession prior to about 1950 was in keeping with a general increase in mean annual temperature and a decrease in precipitation until the early 1940's. A decline in temperature and an increase in precipitation in the 1950's led Collier (1957) to postulate a change from recession to glacial advance in the Cordillera. This predicted advance has not come about in the Canadian Rockies as it has in the Purcells (West and Maki, 1961) and in the Cascades and Olympics (Hubley, 1956). Nevertheless, a marked decline in the rate of recession is evident in the data. Again in the 1960's, there has been an increase of mean annual temperature and a decrease in precipitation (Gardner, 1968b).This trend is not evident in the recession data presented here.

Frontal recession has been accompanied by surface ablation and basal melting resulting in significant volumetric changes in Rocky Mountain glaciers. Within the North Saskatchewan River basin, Henoch (1971) estimated a volume loss of 100×10^6 m^3 (3534×10^7 ft^3) since 1948. He notes that this represents only 4% of the total discharge for the basin in the same period.

Frontal recession is only one aspect of glacier behavior, albeit the most easily studied aspect. Surface velocity has been measured sporadically on the Freshfield (Thorington, 1927), Victoria (Sherzer, 1907) and Saskatchewan (Meier, 1960) glaciers for example. A relatively long record of surface velocity has accumulated since 1945 for the Athabasca glacier. In reviewing this record, Paterson (1964) noted a decline in velocity from 1945 to 1954 followed by a marked increase from 1954 to 1962. He suggested that these long term velocity changes represented the passage of a kinematic wave which occurred in response to the climatic changes noted above.

THE GLACIAL ACTIVITY AND LANDFORMS

Several distinctive landforms have appeared as a result of the recent glacial activity. The landforms are not unique to this area nor are they necessarily unique to this particular glacial episode. Descriptions and analyses of these newly-developed or exposed landforms are few. Sedgewick (1965) and Brunger (1966) described some of the depositional and erosional features exposed by the recession of the Drummond, Hector and Peyto glaciers. Jennings (1951) has done the same for several glaciers in the vicinity of Sunwapta Pass, including the Athabasca. McPherson and Gardner (1969) described subglacially produced features in the vicinity of the Saskatchewan glacier.

As in many other high mountain regions, the terminal and lateral moraines produced during the Neoglacial maximum are amongst the most striking landforms (Figure 3). These moraines are particularly evident in locations formerly occupied by cirque glaciers. Lateral moraines are best preserved on the margins of large valley glaciers such as the Saskatchewan and Freshfield. Indeed, the moraines and the vegetation on them have been utilized in developing a Neoglacial chronology for the region (Heusser, 1956).

The recession of the Saskatchewan glacier exposed a thick deposit of unconsolidated material, probably of pre-Neoglacial origin. The surface morphology of the deposit displays several topographic highs that have been interpreted as pre-Neoglacial features that were overriden. Recent activity of the glacier has subsequently modified these features by superimposing flutings. The result is a landform assemblage somewhat distinct from that developed in the recession of the Drummond and Peyto glaciers for example.

Although the majority of the glaciers have experienced frontal recession producing or exposing classical glacial landforms

Figure 3 - A well-defined Neoglacial terminal
moraine (left centre) and debris covered
terminus of the Wenkchemna Glacier

in the process, several glaciers, notably the Wenkchemna (Figure 3), have undergone stagnation in situ. As noted earlier, this glacier is heavily laden with debris. Comparison of photos indicates the position and form of the terminus has changed little in the last seventy years. However, the surface of the glacier has lowered markedly and the resulting morphology displays many stagnation moraine forms.

CONCLUSION

The Neoglacial period in the Canadian Rocky Mountains has been significant with respect to glacial activity and the associated production of landforms. The maximum stand was probably achieved in the early part of the nineteenth century. This maximum is marked by fresh terminal and lateral moraines. The record of recession, which is relatively detailed for the last seventy years, indicates that recession proceeded slowly until the 1920's. Maximum rates of recession and presumably surface lowering, occurred in the 1940's and early 1950's. Since then there has been a marked decline in the rate though there is no evidence for this becoming a significant readvance. The record does show a relationship with regional climatic trends. Studies of surface velocity on the Athabasca glacier suggest that the climatic changes were manifested in long term changes in velocity.

Landforms produced by the recent glacial activity include the moraines, a variety of small depositional features like kames and "annual" moraines as well as subglacially formed features like flutings. Stagnation features seem to be limited to a few glaciers heavily laden with debris, and in the case of the Wenkchemna, are still in the process of formation.

TABLE I: Glacier Recession Data*

Glacier	Date	Total	Mean Rate	Glacier	Date	Total	Mean Rate
Athabasca	max-1922	270m.	—	Robson	max-1908	280m.	—
	1922-1945	690m.	30.0 m/yr.		1911-1922	86m.	7.8 m/yr.
	1945-1950	96m.	19.2 m/yr.		1922-1931	115m.	12.8 m/yr.
	1950-1956	126m.	21.0 m/yr.		1931-1953	507m.	23.1 m/yr.
	1956-1960	146m.	36.3 m/yr.				
	1960-1964	34m.	8.5 m/yr.				
	1964-1968	19m.	4.8 m/yr.	Saskatchewan	max-1911	120m.	—
					1912-1924	165m.	13.8 m/yr.
Chaba	1927-1936	168m.	18.7 m/yr.		1925-1944	622m.	32.7 m/yr.
					1945-1950	261m.	52.2 m/yr.
Columbia	max-1919	285m.	—		1951-1956	236m.	47.2 m/yr.
	1919-1924	75m.	15.0 m/yr.		1957-1962	223m.	44.8 m/yr.
	1924-1948	810m.	34.0 m/yr.		1963-1966	79m.	26.3 m/yr.
	1948-1958	209m.	42.0 m/yr.		1966-1968	41m.	20.4 m/yr.
Drummond	1884-1906	330m.	15.0 m/yr.	Scott	max-1924	634m.	—
	1906-1920	260m.	18.6 m/yr.		1924-1953	1188m.	41.0 m/yr.
	1920-1930	260m.	26.0 m/yr.				
	1930-1939	340m.	37.9 m/yr.	Victoria	1898-1903	26m.	5.2 m/yr.
	1939-1952	340m.	26.2 m/yr.		1903-1907	15m.	3.8 m/yr.
	1952-1965	325m.	25.0 m/yr.		1907-1912	29m.	5.8 m/yr.
					1931-1945	214m.	15.0 m/yr.
Freshfield	1869-1902	321m.	9.8 m/yr.		1945-1947	20m.	10.0 m/yr.
	1902-1922	278m.	13.9 m/yr.		1947-1949	64m.	32.0 m/yr.
	1922-1926	99m.	24.8 m/yr.		1951-1966	360m.	24.0 m/yr.
	1926-1930	76m.	19.0 m/yr.				
	1930-1934	95m.	23.8 m/yr.	Yoho	max-1901	323m.	—
	1934-1937	124m.	41.3 m/yr.		1901-1904	33m.	11.0 m/yr.
	1937-1944	236m.	38.7 m/yr.		1906-1918	119m.	10.0 m/yr.
	1944-1953	390m.	43.3 m/yr.		1918-1919	15m.	15.0 m/yr.
					1919-1931	165m.	13.8 m/yr.
Hector	1904-1938	396m.	5.9 m/yr.				
	1938-1952	150m.	10.7 m/yr.				
	1952-1965	70m.	5.4 m/yr.				
Lyell	1858-1926	396m.	5.9 m/yr.				
	1926-1930	75m.	19.0 m/yr.				
	1930-1953	1163m.	50.5 m/yr.				
Peyto	1897-1917	115m.	5.7 m/yr.				
	1917-1933	225m.	7.0 m/yr.				
	1933-1936	69m.	23.0 m/yr.				
	1936-1939	90m.	30.0 m/yr.				
	1939-1952	440m.	39.0 m/yr.				
	1952-1965	445m.	34.1 m/yr.				

*Principal sources of these data include: Brunger et. al. (1967), Collier (1957), Field and Heusser (1954), McPherson and Gardner (1969), Nelson et. al. (1966), Sherzer (1907), Wheeler (1931, 1933) and Henoch (1971).

Chapter 2-4

PLEISTOCENE CHRONOLOGY AND GLACIAL GEOMORPHOLOGY: STUDIES IN SOUTHWESTERN BRITISH COLUMBIA.

J. M. Ryder

The topographic diversity of southwestern British Columbia has given rise to a variety of Quaternary glacial land-scapes. Three regions are selected for discussion in order to illustrate contrasting environments and to indicate recent progress in research. The first region, the Lower Fraser Valley, is under-lain by a thick series of Quaternary deposits; it is unique in that it encompasses a large part of the only coastal lowland lying close to the southern limit of Pleistocene ice. The other two regions, a part of the Coast Mountains and a part of the Interior Valleys, are representative of large tracts of the southern and western parts of the province (Figure 1).

THE PLEISTOCENE CHRONOLOGY OF THE LOWER FRASER VALLEY

In the Puget Lowland area of Washington state, where the stratigraphic record is most extensive, four glaciations with intervening interglaciations have been defined (cf. Easterbrook 1969) while at least three glaciations and one well defined inter-glaciation have been recognized in the adjacent Lower Fraser Valley (cf. Armstrong 1957). This interglaciation (Olympia) and the succeeding and final glaciation (Fraser) are common to both areas (Table I) and have been well documented (cf. Armstrong et al 1965).

The Olympia Interglaciation of Lower Fraser Valley is represented by the Quadra sediments. These are fluvial and lacustrine clay, silt and sand, and peat of aggregate thickness ranging from a few to 60 m (200 ft) that were deposited under floodplain and deltaic conditions when sea level was 76 m (250 ft) above present. Plant remains from an extensive section in these beds along the Point Grey sea cliffs (Figure 2) indicate a climate somewhat cooler than at present (Armstrong et al 1965).

Ice of the Vashon Stade of the Fraser Glaciation advanced into the northern end of the Strait of Georgia sometime before 25,000 years B.P. concurrent with valley glaciers of the Evans Creek Stade in the mountains of western Washington. Yet

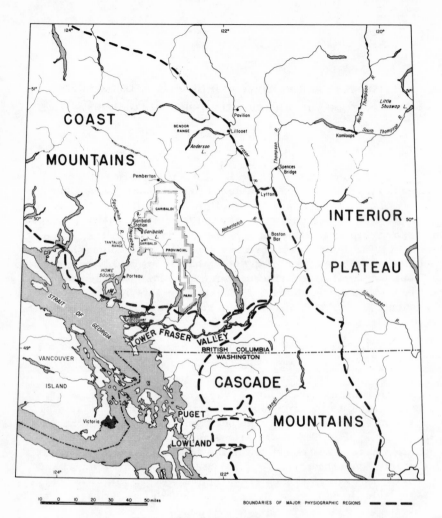

Figure 1 - Location map

it did not reach its maximum extent (terminal position 47°S near Olympia, Washington) until 15,000 years B.P. (Armstrong et al 1965). At this time, ice covered all but the higher peaks of the Coast and Cascade Mountains and occupied the Strait of Georgia. The ice surface stood near 1800 m (6000 ft) at Vancouver, rising to 2100 m (7000 ft) over the Cascade Mountains to the east of Hope (Mathews et al 1970).

Retreat of the Vashon ice was relatively rapid since marine invasion marking the commencement of the Everson Interstade displaced glacial conditions in the western Fraser Lowland only 2000 years after the climax (Armstrong et al 1965).

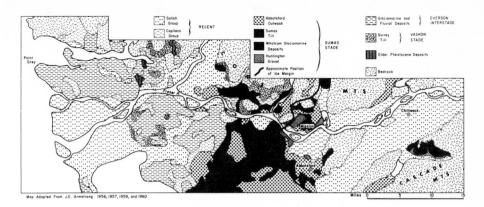

Figure 2 - Surficial geology of the Lower Fraser Valley

Sea-level was high at the time of the Vashon retreat (at least 174 m
(575 ft) at Vancouver, 76 m (250 ft) at Victoria) but underwent
unusually rapid lowering during post-Vashon emergence attributable
to isostatic rebound (Mathews et al 1970).

Sediments of the Everson Interstade (Figure 2) include
fossiliferous stony clays and stony silts interpreted as glacio-
marine drift (Armstrong and Brown 1954) as well as more usual
coastal marine facies (clay, deltaic sand and gravel), fluvial and
lacustrine deposits. The glacio-marine drift is subject to considerable textural and structural variations resulting from sedimentation by the combined agencies of shelf-, berg- and sea-ice,
glacial meltwater and seawater. It is closely associated with and
generally underlies a veneer of beach gravels and littoral sand
formed by reworking of the drift during marine recession
(Armstrong and Brown 1954). The till-like glacio-marine drift is
distinguished from true sub-glacial till by its lesser degree of
compaction, measureable as bulk density or void ratio (Easterbrook
1964).

The extent of ice withdrawal during the Everson Interstade is not known. The presence of an off-shore ice-shelf and
berg-ice, and also the short duration (2000 years) of the interstade,
would suggest that the ice margin was probably adjacent to the
Lower Fraser Valley throughout this interval, and that the Coast
Mountains were continuously glacierized.

The readvance of the Cordilleran ice into the eastern
part of the Lower Fraser Valley as the Sumas Stade was preceeded
and accompanied by up to 150 m (500 ft) of land subsidence. This
second marine incursion extended between 64 and 80 km (40 and 50
mi) inland of the present shoreline to a floating margin of the

65

advancing Sumas ice where a second series of glacio-marine drifts was laid down. During subsequent land emergence, the Sumas ice advanced westwards to its maximum extent (Figure 2) and then withdrew slightly to stand near Sumas and Mission during the construction of a ridge of ice-contact drift before disappearing from the region prior to 9000 years B.P. Emergence of the land continued for a further 6000 years until sea-level stood 10.7 m (35 ft) below present (Mathews et al 1970).

The morphology of Fraser Lowland relates to the glacial history described above and the distribution of Quaternary deposits (Figure 2). The valley floor includes extensive hilly areas rising to between 15 and 335 m (50 and 1100 ft) a.s.l. These uplands consist of either bedrock or, below 122 m (400 ft), pre-Fraser unconsolidated materials that have been irregularly veneered by glacial till or glacio-marine deposits. Glacial outwash and raised marine deltas constitute terraced uplands that rise up to 183 m (600 ft) a.s.l. The hilly areas are separated by broad, flat-floored valleys that are generally below 23 m (75 ft) in elevation. These include the modern floodplain and delta of the Fraser and other lesser rivers that traverse the lowland (Armstrong 1957;1960a & b).

GLACIAL LANDFORMS AND HISTORY OF THE
COAST MOUNTAINS BETWEEN VANCOUVER
AND LILLOOET

During the Vashon Stade of the Fraser Glaciation ice over-rode all but the highest summits in this area. The contrasting form of nunatak horns to subdued ice-rounded summits, together with the distribution of striae and erratics, indicate that the ice surface sloped gradually westward and southward from above 2440 m (8000 ft) in the central and eastern parts of the Coast Mountains to 2100 m (7200 ft) in the vicinity of Garibaldi Lake and 1800 m (6000 ft) at the Tantalus Mountains (Mathews 1950). The regional ice movement was slightly west of south, but with local modifications imposed by ice dispersal from nunatak massifs.

Alpine glacial forms at elevations submerged beneath the climax ice-sheet may post- or pre-date the Vashon maxima. Major valleys may have sufficiently controlled the flow direction of the basal part of the ice sheet that significant valley enlargement took place. A submerged terminal moraine of the Sumas Stade near Porteau in Howe Sound (Mathews et al 1970) indicates that a major valley glacier occupied the Squamish system after the ice-sheet phase, although low-level cirques in the southern Coast Mountains were not reoccupied by alpine glaciers at that time (Mathews 1950).

Most trunk and tributary valleys display typical glacial forms, with the valley side gradients apparently dependant upon the strength of the local bedrock. Thus, for example, the sides of the Squamish River valley are steepest -- with gradients locally reaching to above 80% (39°) -- where it dissects the coarsely jointed granite of the Squamish batholith at the head of Howe Sound. Relatively gentle slopes -- as low as 23% (13°) -- on schistose quartz diorites bound the Cheakamus River valley near Garibaldi Station (Mathews 1958).

Maximum valley erosion took place in "outlet valleys;" that is, those valleys draining most directly from high accumulation zones to the coast, where ice-surface gradients were steepest. Squamish River valley — Howe Sound and other fjord valleys fall into this category. Seismic profiling in Howe Sound indicated a maximum depth of 760 m (2500 ft) to bedrock below 460 m (1500 ft) of unconsolidated sediments (Mathews 1968).

Alpine glacial forms are widespread at high elevations; aretes and horns are best developed on Vashon Stade nunataks. In the Tantalus Mountains (Figure 3), large compound cirques, commonly containing lakes, have floors at elevations between 900 and 1220 m (3000 and 4000 ft). As many as three levels of smaller and higher cirques are related to each of the larger basins. Cirques are presently glacierized above 1500 m (5000 ft) on slopes with a northerly aspect, and above 1825 m (6000 ft) on southerly slopes. In this range "shelf glaciers," consisting of laterally coalescing cirques without sidewalls and truncated by cliff-bands along their lower edges, are common.

Recent studies of cirque morphology and distribution have been carried out by I. S. Evans for selected ranges within the Coast Mountains between Pemberton and Lillooet. He identified a zone of 'asymmetric glaciation' — a narrow altitudinal band between levels of no glaciation and levels of glaciation on all slopes. This has resulted in the relative elongation of north-easterly facing valleys at elevations between 1615 and 1950 m (5300 and 6400 ft) in the Bendor Range of the central southern Coast Mountains. Similar asymmetry was recognized at higher elevations further east and at lower altitudes in more maritime regions (Evans, unpublished data). A marked increase in the elevation of the lower limit of cirque floors is generally apparent eastwards across the Coast Mountains.

The present 'glaciation limit,' (defined as the minimum summit elevation which is required for the formation of glaciers on a mountain) rises northwards across this area from a low of

Figure 3 - Tantalus Mountains from the east in
early spring. Several large cirque
glaciers are visible. The main Tantalus
ridge reaches an elevation of 2,590 m
(8,500 ft.)

Figure 4 - Thompson Valley 12 km (7.5 mi) south
of Ashcroft. In the section exposed above
the railroad tracks, glacio-lacustrine
silt has been terraced and sequentially
overlain by fluvial gravels, aeolian sand
(visible as a thin, light-coloured band),
and alluvial fan mudflows. Most recently,
massive landslides have occurred in the
silt; (an example is visible to the right
of the terraced section).

1900-2000 m (6230-6560 ft) at the head of Howe Sound, to 2600 m
(8530 ft) at the northeastern end of Anderson Lake (Østrem 1966a).
In general, an inverse relationship between the elevation of the
glaciation limit and mean annual precipitation is apparent. Firn
lines are between 100 and 400 m (330 and 1300 ft) lower than the
glaciation limit; maps of these two parameters show similar
isoline patterns. The distribution of ice-cored moraines also
appears to be related to the glaciation limit; they become more
frequent northeastwards across the southern Coast Mountains and
are most common in areas where the glaciation limit lies above
2600 m (8530 ft) (Østrem and Arnold 1970).

From studies in Garibaldi Park, Mathew (1950) has
concluded that existing glaciers are presently retreating from
climaxes attained in the early part of the eighteenth century and the
middle of the nineteenth century. These maxima mark their
greatest expansion since late-Pleistocene time. Scattered data
from elsewhere in the Coast Mountains suggest similar fluctuations.

Quaternary vulcanism during the existence of extensive
ice cover gave rise to unusual glacially modified volcanic forms.
The relationship of volcanic to glacial features suggests that Mount
Garibaldi was largely constructed after the climax of the Fraser
Glaciation but during the existence of residual ice below 1340 m
(4400 ft) in the Squamish River Valley. The western section of the
volcanic cone was built upon the ice and slumped into the valley
upon melting (Mathews 1952a). Lavas from other associated
volcanic centres in Garibaldi Park display typical flow forms at
higher elevations, but were ponded against valley ice to form
unusually thick termini with steep concave faces (Mathews 1952b).
In the Cheakamus River valley north of Garibaldi Station several
anomalously narrow and steep-sided flows resemble eskers in their
outward form. They possibly resulted from the movement of lava
through trenches or tunnels melted in residual valley ice
(Mathews 1958).

LATE-PLEISTOCENE AND EARLY POST-
GLACIAL DEVELOPMENT OF THE INTERIOR
VALLEYS

The Interior Valleys of southern British Columbia are
characteristically steep-sided trenches formed by pre-Pleistocene
rivers and modified only slightly by glacial erosion. Aggradation
by major rivers during and following deglaciation, and later
dissection of this valley-fill, took place in response to the varying
availability of glacially derived materials and the control of this
upon the behaviour of the rivers. The landforms produced by these
processes dominate the landscapes of many Interior Valleys at the
present time.

During deglaciation extensive pro-glacial lakes developed
in valleys where natural drainage ways were blocked by active
glaciers or stagnant ice. Within the valley of the present South
Thompson River, glacial Lake Thompson was impounded between
retreating tongues of ice in the valleys of the Thompson and North
Thompson Rivers and Shuswap Lake (Mathews 1944). Up to 150 m
(500 ft) of glacio-lacustrine silt, an estimated 9.2 km^3 (2.2 mi^3)
(Fulton 1965), was deposited along a 58 km (36 mi) stretch of the
South Thompson Valley to the east of Kamloops. Extremely high
depositional rates for the silt (derived from recently exposed
glacial drift) are indicated by the presence of 6 m (20 ft) thick
varves in the lower part of the unit. The gradual fining upwards
of the varves to beds about 2.5 cm (1 in) in thickness reflects a
gradual decrease in sedimentation rates corresponding to a
gradual retreat of the ice fronts and decline in sediment availability
(Fulton 1965).

Glacial Lake Thompson expanded in accord with ice withdrawal from the valley of the Thompson River, while the lake
level fell from an initial high of 500 m (1635 ft) to a final low of
375 m (1230 ft) a.s.l., (water levels approximate due to isostatic
tilting) (Fulton 1969). Glacio-lacustrine silts (locally interbedded
with deltaic gravel) extend from Kamloops down the Thompson
valley to Skoonka Creek 6.4 km (4 mi) south of Spences Bridge,
where the final ice barrier for this lake was situated (Anderton
1970). The silt valley-fill was later dissected, terraced and
veneered with fluvial cobble gravels during post-glacial degradation, and the silt is now exposed in terrace bluffs throughout the
valley (Figure 4).

Fluvial aggradation was the dominant infilling process of
the lower Thompson valley over a distance of 28 km (16 mi) between
Botanie Creek near Lytton and Skhpowtz near Spences Bridge.
Over 150 m (500 ft) of gravel with some sand was deposited in
early post-glacial time. The deposit shows cross-bedding
structures that typically result from channel migration in
braided streams. Angular talus fragments of local bedrock
occur within the gravels, especially within the lower 30 m (100 ft)
and range in size from pebbles to masses of landslide proportions,
indicating the general instability of the valley sides following ice
withdrawal. Also, the lithologies of better rounded clasts suggest
that much of the gravel originated from local lateral sources by
reworking of glacial drift and rapid weathering (Anderton 1970).
Anderton suggests that the accumulation of the entire gravel unit
may well have taken place within less than 1000 years.

Within the Fraser Valley between Boston Bar and
Pavilion, sequences of fluvial and fluvio-glacial gravel together

70

Table I. Pleistocene sequence in British Columbia and suggested correlations

WISCONSIN STAGE

Puget Lowland	Fraser Lowland	Interior British Columbia	Midcontinental U.S.A.
10,000 Sumas Stade	9,000 (?)*	9,000 late-glacial readvance	7,500 Valderan
11,000 Everson Interstade	11,000 (?)	(?)	11,000 Two Creekan
13,000 Vashon Stade	13,000	major glaciation (Vashon Stade)	13,000 Woodfordian
Evans Creek Stade 18,000			
OLYMPIA INTERGLACIATION 29,000 (?)	25,000	20,000	22,500 FARMDALIAN
	36,000 (?)	major interglacial (OLYMPIA INTERGLACIATION) 40,000	
SALMON SPRINGS GLACIATION 40,000	SEMIAMU GLACIATION	major glaciation	ALTONIAN 40,000
PUYALLUP INTERGLACIATION			
STUCK GLACIATION	SEYMOUR GLACIATION (age unknown)		SANGAMONIAN STAGE
ALDERTON INTERGLACIATION			
ORTINGTON GLACIATION			

FRASER GLACIATION

WISCONSIN STAGE

*Radio-carbon dates are given as absolute age in years. Those for the Sumas Stade in Fraser Lowland are currently undergoing revision. Boundaries between geologic-climatic units are time transgressive.

Source: Armstrong 1957, Armstrong et al. 1965, Easterbrook 1969 for Puget and Fraser Lowlands; Armstrong and Fulton 1965, Fulton 1969, Tipper 1971 for Interior British Columbia; Frye, Willman and Black 1965, for Midcontinental U.S.A.

71

with glacio-lacustrine silt and sand attest to processes of aggradation similar to those described above. However, many riverbank sections show tilted and contorted silt beds that are commonly overlain by till. This would suggest that the valley was reoccupied by ice following a glacio-lacustrine interval. Certain tributary valleys, notably that of the Nahatlatch River, contain thick sequences of dissected, but otherwise undisturbed silt or gravel that was apparently laid down in pro-glacial lakes blocked by ice in the Fraser Valley. It would seem that this valley was subject to a late-glacial ice readvance that may be correlative with the Sumas Stade of the Fraser Glaciation (Table I).

During and following the post-glacial aggradational phase of the major rivers, deposition of reworked glacial drift and locally weathered material from tributary valleys formed alluvial fans upon constructional benches, terraces and flood-plains (Figure 4). The Mazama volcanic ash bed, deposited some 6600 years ago (Wilcox and Powers 1964), commonly occurs in fans with an average depth of burial of 2 m (6 ft). This indicates that most fan aggradation took place during the first three millenia following general deglaciation of the Interior Plateau (Fulton 1969) in accord with the paraglacial nature of the sedimentation process (Ryder 1971). Most recently, dissection of the fans has taken place along with widespread degradation by major rivers.

SECTION THREE

SLOPE PROCESSES AND MORPHOLOGY

Chapter 3-1

DEBRIS ACCRETION ON TALUS SLOPES
IN THE CENTRAL YUKON TERRITORY.

James T. Gray*

The objectives of this paper are to describe improved methods of measurement of different processes of debris transport down steep mountain slopes, and to present the principal results of these measurements for sites in the Ogilvie and Wernecke Mountains, central Yukon Territory. The general location of these sites is shown in Figure 1. The western zone is referred to as the Tombstone area; the eastern zone as the Bear River area.

The mountain slopes studied range in elevation from 1500 m - 2500 m, (4800 ft - 8000 ft) and are in a periglacial zone, characterised by long cold winters, short, cool summers and relatively low year round precipitation.

The study concentrated in part on the varying importance of the processes in different lithological zones. Impressive contrasts were revealed between the mountain slopes in the syenitic to monzonitic intrusion in the Tombstone area and those in the metasedimentaries of both areas.

The individual mountain slopes may be divided into a steep upper zone, consisting predominantly of rock walls and buttresses, and a more gently graded basal zone, with an extensive talus cover (Figure 2). Debris transport can be considered as the transfer of debris over the surface of the upper zone, the basal zone, or across the boundary between the two zones. The scope of this paper is restricted to the latter. It is, in effect, concerned with primary debris accretion on the talus slopes and provides information on rates of recent erosion on the upper rock wall zone, and on the relative importance of the different processes which transport debris from the rock walls to the talus slopes.

---

*The financial support of the Arctic Institute of North America and the Geological Survey of Canada is gratefully acknowledged.

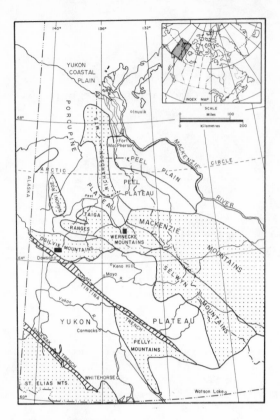

Figure 1 - Location Map

Figure 2 - Rock walls and talus slopes in metasediments in the Bear River area.

METHODS OF MEASUREMENT

The greatest difficulty in measuring debris accretion is created by the frequent disturbance of the talus surface. A lichen cover rarely has a chance to develop on old talus, and so differentiation of freshly accreted debris from old debris is very difficult. To overcome this problem researchers have measured debris accretion on a variety of marker surfaces, e.g. on snow covered talus surfaces, (Caine, 1969; Gardner, 1970a), on squares of sacking or plastic, (Rapp, 1960b; Gardner, 1968a; Caine, 1969; Luckman, 1971), and on large elevated boulders which can be swept clean prior to measurement, (Luckman, 1971). These methods have only had a qualified degree of success in obtaining the total picture of current debris accretion on the slopes of any region. The limitations of marker surfaces of snow are that they do not exist during the summer and so only the winter and spring debris accretion can be measured. Squares of sacking or plastic have inevitably covered negligibly small areas of talus slopes. They have also received an unknown quantity of debris from higher points on the talus slope in addition to that quantity representing true accretion from the rock wall above. In addition they have been very susceptible to natural destruction. Large elevated boulders only trap debris when a thick snow cover exists on the talus slopes.

In order to minimise these difficulties it has been necessary, in the present research, to adapt and use a wide range of techniques to measure accretion at various seasons on different types of rock walls and talus slopes.

Debris Accretion on Continuous Snow Surfaces

On June 18th, 1969, newly fallen debris was measured on the deeply snow covered basal slopes of a high steep syenite rock wall in the Tombstone area. Figure 3 is a diagrammatic view, from the north, of the main features of the rock wall and sampled snow slope. The snow slope was divided into zone A, situated below a steep chimney on the north wall and zone B, situated between this chimney and a deep cleft on the west wall at the head of the cirque. The rock wall averages 70° in inclination and is too steep to sustain the build-up of a thick snow cover. Avalanching is therefore of insignificant importance, and the debris on the snow slope was regarded as entirely derived by rock-fall.

The method involved measurement of the 'a,' 'b,' and 'c' axes of fallen particles and conversion to volumes using empirical equations relating particle volume to the product of the three axes. Derivation of these equations for 74 syenite, 100 dolomite and 140 orthoquartzite particles suggests that, in the aggregate, the volume

77

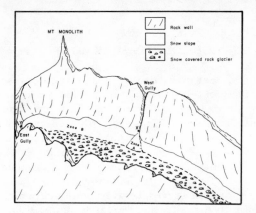

Figure 3 - Rock wall and snow slope at locality TL 4,
    Tombstone area. (Mean wall height: 430 m;
    length xy: 475 m; mean rock wall angle 70°)

of particles is approximately 0.5 to 0.6 times the product of the
three axes. The weight of the particles is then calculated as the
product of the volume and an approximate density of 2.7 gm/cc.
The volumes were then totalled to get the debris accretion on the
entire snow slope. The area of the rock wall from which this debris
was derived was photogrammetrically measured and an estimate of
its mean rate of recession during the spring of 1969 was obtained.

Debris Accretion on Lichenous Surfaces

Below several syenite walls the talus zone consists
merely of a narrow fringe of large boulders and cobbles interspersed with vegetated patches of fine gravel. Because of the steep
walls and lack of gullies there are no avalanche processes to redistribute this coarse talus, and lichen cover has a chance to
become established. Occasionally there are fresh rock-falls onto
these slopes and if rock-fall has occurred within the last few
decades the large particles involved can be identified by their
sparse or non-existent lichen cover.

The volumes of such particles may be calculated using
the previously discussed method of axis measurement. If the sizes
of the largest lichens of a given species are measured on each
particle and if a lichen growth rate is available for the talus environment, a reasonable estimate can be made of the volume of debris
which has fallen during certain time intervals in the recent past.

A lichen growth rate of 35 mm (1.4 in)/century, with a
ten to fifteen year colonisation interval was established for the
largest five lichens of the species Rhizocarpon geographicum
(sensu latu) by sampling at dated sites on the Klondike gold tailings
near Dawson City. The sampling and measurement procedures

78

were patterned on a combination of methods described by Beschel (1961) and Stork (1963). Extrapolation of these rates from the Klondike site at 350 m (1120 ft) to the climatically more severe talus environment at 1000 - 1500 m (3200 - 4800 ft) is problematical. It is evident, however, that the rate of 35 mm (1.4 in)/ century is a maximum growth rate for R. geographicum on the talus slopes. The minimum colonisation period may be taken as about fifteen years.

Using this maximum growth rate and minimum colonisation interval, volumes of rock-fall derived debris, over certain minimum time intervals, were calculated for two rock walls in the Tombstone syenite zone. From these results and knowing the areas of the source walls, maximum rates of erosion in recent years were also assessed.

Debris Accretion in Avalanche Deposits

Debris content of sample areas in four of the most debris laden avalanche deposits in the zone of metasedimentaries was assessed. All measurements were necessarily made on surficial debris. Therefore the estimated volumes of debris are subject to possible error from neglect of buried debris. Pits were dug at three points where the surface exhibited a dense debris cover, but debris was not observed at depth.

Avalanches were relatively infrequent within the igneous instrusive zone. Those that did occur usually consisted of fresh, debris free snow, originating from chimneys and ledges on the rock walls.

Debris Accretion Due to Debris Flows

Debris flows result from conditions of moisture saturation of a weathered mantle or local talus accumulations in rock wall gullies. Such a flow may result from an intense summer rainstorm or more probably as a result of the release of a special type of slush avalanche, described by Rapp (1960a), as a torrent avalanche.

In the field areas the morphological features associated with the debris flows, e.g. debris tongues, distributary lobes and levees, are present on a number of talus slopes below gently inclined rock walls at lower elevations, but are generally absent below the steep rock walls at higher elevations. If debris flows have occurred on the latter slopes the evidence has been obliterated by subsequent snow avalanches.

Debris flows have been of particular importance in one locality in the Tombstone area (Figure 4) where the bedrock slope has a relatively low angle of 36° and is mantled by a thick cover of weathered detritus. At intervals the slope is marked by long straight gashes, where torrent avalanches and/or summer rainstorms have caused erosion down to the unweathered bedrock. From the bed of these gullies the weathered mantle can be seen to reach a depth of up to 6 m (19 ft). In order to illustrate the quantitative importance of one of these debris flows, the minimum net volume of one of the tongues was calculated.

Debris Accretion on Nets

Measurement of debris accretion on snow surfaces and in avalanche deposits does not give information concerning the effective morphological activity on rock walls during late spring or summer after the snow cover has gone. Lichenometry could only be used to measure maximum volumes produced by large rock-falls on certain slopes within the Tomstone intrusion. Therefore it was decided to install nets in 1968 on two talus cones (6820 and 6830) in order to examine debris accretion resulting from all processes during the fall to spring period in 1968-69 and during the summer period in 1969. The distribution of the net on cone 6830 is illustrated in Figure 5.

The net material is cotton, heavily creosoted to resist rotting in damp conditions. When stretched out on the slope, the mean mesh size in a downslope direction is 2.5 cm (1 in) and in a direction across the slope 0.7 cm (0.3 in). Since only a small proportion of particles finer than the mesh size are present on the talus cone surfaces, the debris filtered through the net mesh may be neglected.

Figure 4 - Net for debris collection on talus cone 6830.

Figure 5 - Recent debris flows in weathered syenites

The nets were anchored firmly to bedrock at the apices of the cones by means of rock bolts and cables, and to several points on the talus surface by attachment to large embedded boulders. The weight of the material tended to hold the nets in place in any case. When stretched out, they covered a rectangular strip extending from the apex to the base of each talus cone. The total sample area for cone 6820 was 225 m^2, (2400 ft^2), i.e. 12.4% of the cone area; for cone 6830 it was 1435 m^2 (15,500 ft^2), i.e. 12.8% of the cone area.

The principal assumption of the method, invalid for small isolated squares of sacking and plastic used by previous workers, is that the debris on the nets has been derived from the rock wall zone. Therefore the nets had to be of sufficient width to preclude avalanches from acquiring debris from the talus surface and depositing it on the net at a lower point. They were also placed in such a position that they filled the narrow sections of the cones between the buttresses guarding the entrances to the rock wall gullies. The net on cone 6820 has a width of 3 m (10 ft); that on cone 6830 has a width of 8 m (26 ft). It is still possible for avalanches to move downslope at a slight angle from the fall line, strip debris from the uncovered talus on one side of the net and deposit it on the net itself. Then the debris found on the net would give a false indication of debris accretion on the cone. In order to establish whether or not this happened over the period 1968-69, 25 cm (10 in) wide bands of talus were painted down the edge of the netting on cone 6830 in 1968, with the aim of assessing, upon re-examination of the slope, whether or not disturbance of debris at the edge of the net by avalanches occurred. These lines remained undisturbed over the first period of measurement and indicated that none of the debris was derived in this manner. In the summer of 1969 lines were painted along the edges of the netting on cone 6820 for future reference.

PRINCIPAL RESULTS

The principal results of the debris accretion measurements are presented in Table I. Rates of recent rock wall erosion were derived where possible by dividing volumes of debris accretion by the respective rock wall areas. They may be tentatively compared with rates of rock wall erosion in the region over a 10,000 to 14,000 year postglacial interval (Table II). There is a general indication in such a comparison that the currently observed level of operation of geomorphic processes is insufficient to account for the postglacial talus accumulations. Large scale events, of more infrequent occurrence than those for which observations or measurements have been made in the field areas, are probably responsible for an increase in the mean rate of postglacial rock

TABLE I : RECENT DEBRIS ACCRETION ON THE BASAL PARTS OF ROCK WALLS IN THE OGILVIE AND WERNECKE MOUNTAINS, YUKON TERRITORY

Process	Technique	Locality	Rock wall lithology	Date measured	Accretion period	Debris volume estimate (m³)	Erosion rate mm/1000 yrs	Precision of erosion rate mm/1000 yrs	Comments
Rock-falls									
1	measurement on snow surface	TL4 Tombstone	syenite & monzonite	18/6/69	1-6 months	1.54	3	1-6	Complete slope sampled
2	lichenometry	TL5 Tombstone	"	8/8/69	>10 years	37.56	<19	<19	"
3	lichenometry	cone 6830 Tombstone	"	24/8/68	>10 years	37.56	<8	<8	Very large rock-falls only
Snow avalanches									
1	debris in avalanche deposits	TL2 Tombstone	quartzite minor slate	21/6/67	1-4 weeks	1.79	57	20-200	
2	"	BL4 Bear River	"	12/6/68	1-4 weeks	0.17-0.34	9-17	3-30	
3	"	BL3 cone 6801 Bear River	"	4/6/68	1-4 weeks	0.60	3	?	
Slow debris shift									
1	measurement on net	cone 6820 Bear River	dolomite	20/7/69	1 year	0.36	1	0-2	
Debris flow									
1	vol. measurement of debris tongue	TL6 Tombstone	syenite & monzonite	9/6/67	18 years	158	—	—	Special localities only
All processes									
1	measurement on net	cone 6820 Bear River	dolomite	20/7/69	1 year	1.148	44.3	10-100	12.5% of cone area sampled
2	"	cone 6830 Tombstone		14/8/69	1 year	0.428	8.8	3-30	"

wall erosion and talus development.

This view is supported by evidence contained in a rock glacier in the Tombstone area. The rock glacier surface is covered with boulders, which have been entirely derived from the rock wall on the south side of the cirque. A traverse, from the largest tributary talus cones to the front of the rock glacier, revealed a zone in the middle of the rock glacier, where the boulders are of unusually large size (≥ 10 m (33 ft) in length) as compared with the boulders around it. These blocks are clearly the product of one or several unusually large scale rock-falls in the postglacial period. The distance of the boulders from the base of the source wall and the sizes of thalli of the lichen species R. geographicum on the surfaces suggests that these very large scale rock-falls occurred at least 400 years B.P. The distribution of debris sizes on the rock glacier surface indicates that there was a long time span before and since the deposition of this very large debris, during which lesser rock-falls occurred.

The quantitative evidence from the snow covered slope, illustrated in Figure 3 suggests that erosion represented by rock-falls on the syenite walls is very irregular in the spatial dimension as well as in the time dimension. It has been about thirty times greater in the narrow gully above zone A than on the smooth wall above zone B.

The data in Table I indicate the much greater geomorphic significance of a single debris flow as compared with more frequent events such as avalanches and rock-falls. Rapp (1960a, p. 185) concluded for a mountain zone in northern Sweden that slush avalanches on gentle slopes and torrent avalanches on steep slopes are far more effective as agents of transport than all rock-falls and dirty avalanches. But in the Ogilvie and Wernecke Mountains evidence of debris flows on the slopes was limited only to moderately inclined slopes on the north side of Tombstone valley, covered with deeply frost weathered bedrock, and to well dis-sected rock walls of relatively low inclination in the Bear River area. The processes leading to debris flow, viz. torrent avalanches and ephemeral run-off are not considered to be significant on the steep rock walls when compared with rock-falls and snow avalanches.

In the igneous intrusives of the Tombstone area, avalanching is considered to be of minor importance as compared with rock-falls. Avalanche deposits were not noted on the snow covered syenite talus slopes in this zone. Indeed the rock walls are too steep to permit the build-up of a snow pack which could release spring avalanches, or to permit the accumulation of a potential debris load for such avalanches as do occur.

83

Even in the metasedimentary zone, where they are of frequent occurrence in the spring, most of the observed avalanches were debris free. The dirtiest avalanches contained between 0.17 and 1.79 m^3 (6 - 63 ft^3) of debris, which corresponds to mean erosion rates two to ten times slower than the mean postglacial rate of erosion by all processes for metasediments.

Frequent small rock-falls have been observed in the gullies above the talus cones after summer rain showers and these certainly augment debris accretion on the talus slopes. But on the basis of one year's measurements on cones 6820 and 6830, it is evident that the summer of 1969 has been of less importance than the previous fall, winter and spring for debris accretion resulting from small scale events.

Slow shift of debris from the gully zone, amounting to 0.036 m^3 (1.3 ft^3) in one year, has been observed at the top of cone 6820. This total is about 1/30th of the total estimated accretion for the talus cone for that year, which suggests that debris shift may be a process of only slight importance to debris accretion.

TABLE II

Rates of Recession During a Probable Postglacial
Interval of 10,000 -14,000 years in the Ogilvie and
Wernecke Mountains

Lithology	No. of Rock Walls	Range of recession rates (mm/1,000yr)[1]	Mean recession rate (mm/1000 yrs)
Metasedimentary mainly quartzites dolomites and slates	8	20 - 170	73
Igneous - syenite and diabase	2	7 - 30	18.5

Source: Gray, 1971, pp. 21-35.

[1]Recession rates are calculated normal to the rock wall surface

Chapter 3-2

SOME OBSERVATIONS ON THE EROSION OF TALUS SLOPES
BY SNOW AVALANCHES IN SURPRISE VALLEY,
JASPER NATIONAL PARK, ALBERTA.

B. H. Luckman*

During the past four years the author has been engaged
in a study of talus slopes and talus slope processes in Surprise
Valley, a small alpine valley near Maligne Lake, Jasper National
Park, Alberta. One of the major projects, started in 1968,
involves the measurement of the accumulation of debris on cleaned
boulder surfaces and polyethelene squares spread over the talus
surface (see Luckman, 1971, for a brief discussion of the techniques
used). As the study progressed it became apparent that, as well as
rockfall and snow avalanche deposition from the cliffs, considerable
amounts of material were also being moved downslope as a result
of avalanche erosion of the talus surface itself. This paper
examines the nature of this erosional activity and discusses some
of its effects on the development of talus slopes.

Snow avalanches are rapid downslope movements of snow
caused by failure in the snow cover of a slope. Although there is
an extensive literature on their classification, prediction and
causes (e.g. International Association of Scientific Hydrology,
1966), their importance as a geomorphic process was not clearly
demonstrated until the publication of Rapp's detailed studies of
their activity in the Alps and Scandinavia (Rapp, 1958, 1959,
1960a). More recently, White (1968), Gardner (1967, 1970a),
Potter (1968) and Luckman (1971) have reported similar activity
from the American Cordillera which confirm and extend Rapp's
observations.

EVIDENCE FROM SURPRISE VALLEY

General Observations

The amount of erosion accomplished by a particular
avalanche depends on the character of the avalanche and the thickness
and condition of the snow cover on the talus slope at the time. Many

*The financial support of McMaster University, the
Government of Ontario and the National Research Council of Canada
is gratefully acknowledged.

85

avalanches merely redistribute the surface snow and do not come
into contact with the underlying talus. Examination of recent
avalanches and avalanche snow indicates that erosion may be
carried out by spring avalanches of wet snow from the cliffs or by
slab avalanches on the slope itself. The latter may be triggered by
small avalanches from the cliffs, cornice falls or simply the
instability of the snow on the slope. The resulting erosional
patterns are similarly varied; examples from Surprise Valley
indicate that erosion may be widespread (Figure 1) or restricted
to a narrow zone and in some cases only a small part of the track.
At one location the marker boulders[1] from an eroded square were
carried directly over an undisturbed square and deposited a further
40 m (130 ft) downslope.

There is also considerable variation in the pattern of
avalanche activity at any site from year to year. This can be
illustrated by a brief summary of the results from one site, the
Tumblin' Creek Cone.

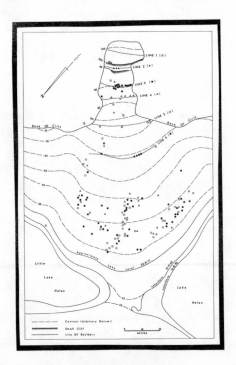

Figure 1 - The displacement of boulders from the
six lines on the Tumblin' Creek Cone (July 1971).

_____

[1]So-called because marked with paint.

The Tumblin' Creek Cone

     This cone is an avalanche boulder tongue of the "fan" type (Rapp, 1959) built out into Lake Helen and fed by a chute cut into benched cliffs of Mississippian limestones (Figure 1). The cone has dense cover of sample boulders and squares and additional information on avalanche erosion was sought from six lines of painted boulders laid across the throat of the cone in September 1969. This area of the cone often develops an ice carapace in winter from the freezing of a small stream flowing from a spring at the head of the cone. In 1969-70 this appears to have protected the lines as, although there was considerable erosion in the area below the lowest line (between 55 and 70 m (180 and 230 ft) contours),[2] there was only a small amount of movement from the lines, most of which could have been the result of rockfall impact (Table I). In 1970-71 however (Figure 1), a large part of the surface debris in the chute and upper part of the cone was picked up by an avalanche (together with 18 of the 20 sample boulders in this area and the top nine squares) and deposited half way down the scree. Parts of the upper three lines which survived (Table I) were all in the western half of the cone where they were possibly protected by ice. Though a complete search was impossible due to the high level of the lake in 1971, most of the boulders were recovered between the 50 and 60 m (165 and 195 ft) "contours," overlapping the main erosional zone of 1969-70. Since the debris from the lines, destroyed squares and sample sites was all deposited in the same area, Figure 1 has been simplified and only shows the boulders which moved from the six lines.

     The main depositional zone in both 1968 and 1970 was much lower down the cone (35 - 50 m (115 - 165 ft) "contours") whereas in 1969 the relatively small amount of deposition was mainly on the highest part of the cone (above 60 m (195 ft), see Luckman, 1971, Figure 9).

     These results suggest an overlapping of erosional and depositional zones from year to year producing a net downslope shift of the surface debris on the cone over a long period of time.

Amounts of Movement

     The direct measurement of the volumes of eroded talus material incorporated into avalanches is very difficult without either marking the whole scree surface or the immediate

---

[2]Elevation above arbitrary datum.

TABLE I: Displacement of boulders from the six lines on the Tumblin' Creek Cone

Line	Boulders set	Period of Measurement	Remaining on line	Movement			Lost
				2m	10m	10m	
1	29	1969 - 70	15	5	4	2	3
		1970 - 71	16		2	7	4
2	29	1969 - 70	25	3	0	0	1
		1970 - 71	16		4	1	8
3	31	1969 - 70	21	6	0	1	3
		1970 - 71	12		2	12	5
4	30	1969 - 70	26	3	0	1	0
		1970 - 71	6		1	20	3
5	40	1969 - 70	31	2	4	4	0
		1970 - 71	3		1	35	1
6	50	1969 - 70	39	3	1	7	0
		1970 - 71	5		0	36	9

NOTE: The lines were not reset in 1970. The results should be examined in conjunction with Figure 1 which illustrates the spatial pattern of deposition in 1971. The data in the table are grouped for convenient comparision of the two years.

examination of fresh avalanche debris. Table II presents selected data showing the amount and extent of deposition at the seven major sites studied. These figures should be considered minimum values since there is a bias at most sites towards sample site locations near the base of the scree and the boulder sites only measure debris which ablates from a snow cover.

The data in Table II show wide variations in the extent and volume of deposition both in terms of year to year variation at the same site and the relative amounts of variation between different sites in successive years. Though it is not possible to differentiate the deposits of avalanche erosion from other sources, all the sites where evidence of avalanche erosion occurs have considerably higher values of accumulation in the range of 0.5 - 8.0 mm (0.02 - 0.3 in)/yr.[3] Most of this deposition would appear to be the results of the erosional redistribution of debris by avalanches and in the major depositional areas of the scree considerably greater thicknesses may occur. For example, a square (2.32m^2; 25 ft^2) at the lower end of the avalanche boulder tongue at Old Nip received an average thickness of 15.80, 12.17 and 2.17 mm (0.62, 0.48 and 0.08 in) in the three years.

The wide variations in the amounts and frequency of avalanche erosion shown by this data suggest that each site may have its own magnitude-frequency spectrum of significant erosional events (compare, for example, E.V.S., Surprise II and Strike Valley). The main differences between the sites are in the intensity and frequency of avalanche activity rather than its presence or absence: all of the sites except the Entrance scree showed evidence of avalanche erosion at least once in the period 1968-1971.

COMPARISON OF ROCKFALL CONE AND AVALANCHE BOULDER TONGUE

Like most other data on geomorphic processes, these observations only encompass a relatively brief period in the development of the landforms. However, inferences about the long term effects of these processes may be tested by comparing the sedimentological characteristics of similar avalanche and non-avalanche slopes to examine the effects of avalanche modification over an extended period of time. An excellent opportunity for such a comparison occurs at Old Nip where an avalanche boulder tongue of

---

[3]The figure for Strike Valley in 1971 is inflated by the inclusion of a boulder of 1.03m^3 (35 ft^3) from one of the sample sites.

TABLE II: Summary Statistics for Deposition on Sample Boulders and Squares in Surprise Valley 1969 - 1971

| | | | | | | % Sites with Deposition | | |
| | | | | | | (a) | (b) | (c) |
Site	Year	Dominant Process	Number of Sites	Area (m^2)	Average Thickness[1] $(mm^2\ yr^{-1})$	0.001 $(cm.^3\ m^{-2})$	1.0 $(cm.^3\ m^{-2})$	mean $(cm.^3\ m^{-2})$
E.V.S.	1969	Av	141	60.7	0.23	75.5	7.7	12.7
E.V.S.	1970	Av	139	53.5	0.18	82.7	5.0	8.6
E.V.S.	1971	Ave	126	42.9	4.00	27.8	35.8	24.6
Entrance	1969	R	39	22.6	0.26	61.5	5.1	12.6
Entrance	1970	R	36	15.6	0.06	75.0	5.6	16.7
Entrance	1971	R/Avs	36	15.6	0.15	39.0	5.6	13.9
Palliser	1969	R/Av	124	91.0	0.42	75.0	3.2	3.2
Palliser	1970	R	150	104.8	0.13	87.2	2.0	3.0
Palliser	1971	Ave	132	65.1	0.94	58.3	12.1	12.1
Old Nip	1969	R/Ave	65	49.4	1.52	78.5	6.2	6.2
Old Nip	1970	R/Ave	70	61.0	0.61	61.4	5.7	5.7
Old Nip	1971	R/Ave	66	48.8	2.68	31.9	33.3	21.2
Strike Valley	1969	Ave	58	43.5	3.33	39.6	22.4	20.7
Strike Valley	1970	Ave	57	42.7	3.91	25.0	36.7	17.6
Strike Valley	1971	Ave	59	42.9	24.82	37.3	18.6	1.7
T.C. cone	1969	R/Av	93	54.8	2.51	30.0	20.4	17.2
T.C. cone	1970	Ave	255	125.2	5.59	8.2	41.6	18.9
T.C. cone	1971	Ave	183	84.3	7.99	14.8	36.4	15.9
T.C. area	1969	R/Av	81	40.7	0.19	44.4	2.5	16.0
T.C. area	1970	R/Av	74	38.8	0.95	46.1	13.6	14.9
T.C. area	1971	R/Av	67	36.4	0.21	62.7	4.5	11.9
Surprise II	1969	Ave	170	106.9	2.08	31.8	20.6	14.1
Surprise II	1970	Avc	261	160.8	0.97	8.3	11.3	12.3
Surprise II	1971	Av	234	139.6	0.94	32.1	9.4	10.3

NOTES:

E.V.S.	Eastern Valley Side	T.C.	Tumblin' Creek
*Av	avalanche, R = Rockfall		
Ave	avalanche erosion of sites		
Avc	main avalanche debris from cliff		
Avs	minor avalanche activity		

[1]Total accumulation / Total sampled area

the "roadbank" type (Rapp, 1959) has been developed on the northern flank of a large rockfall cone.

Four sampling profiles were taken, two on the cone and two on the tongue, with two samples of fifty stones taken at each sampling site. Details of the sampling design are given in Luckman, (1970); the size measure given here is the side of a cube of equivalent volume to the product of the measured lengths of three perpendicular axes and a shape factor.

There are considerable differences in the sedimento-logical character of the two slopes (Figure 2). The rockfall cone has much coarser material and a smaller sorting gradient. On the avalanche slope, apart from the top two sites, the sorting gradient

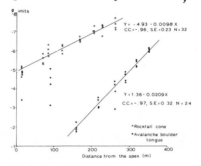

Figure 2 - Relationship between mean grainsize and distance from the apex of the Old Nip Cone for samples of 50 stones.

is much steeper and some of the debris is quite small. Avalanching appears to have removed the loose, coarser fraction from the upper and middle parts of the track exposing the finer material which occurs at depth. Although this has more cohesion and is less easily eroded, it is also more susceptible to fluvial activity and the whole range of small scale slope and periglacial processes. In the lower part of the slope the deposition of large amounts of relatively small material considerably reduces the mean grain size in comparison to the rockfall slope. The anomalous nature of the upper two sites on the tongue is probably due to the avalanches beginning some distance away from the apex of the cone since they are slab avalanches which are triggered by the impact of cornice falls from the top of the 3 - 400 m (1000 - 1300 ft) cliff.

The sedimentary characteristics shown by this avalanche slope are clearly the result of the long term operation of processes similar to those described from Tumblin' Creek. The major role of avalanches on such slopes is the erosion and downslope transfer of the surface talus material, i.e., these avalanches act as a "queueing" process (Thornes, 1971). There are two major con-sequences of this activity. Firstly, the generally "smooth"

91

appearance of the talus surface in the erosional part of the track as a result of the removal of the loose debris. Secondly, the production of basal concavity where there is heavy deposition at the base of the slope. The latter observation is similar to the results generated by Caine's (1969) model of talus evolution by slush avalanches except that, in his examples from New Zealand, the slush avalanches are redistributing winter rockfall material deposited on the snow rather than eroding the talus. However since slush and wet snow avalanches are part of the same continuum, only minor modifications would be needed to the model to allow for the incorporation of talus material into the basal part of the avalanches.

Both of these characteristics are common to avalanche boulder tongues which develop where erosional activity is strongly localised and there is a plentiful supply of debris. Where avalanche activity is less frequent or the avalanche tracks more variable the results may range from incipient tongues developed on the scree to barely perceptible "smoothed" areas or areas of "balanced boulders" (Rapp, 1960a; Gardner, 1970a) indicating avalanche deposition.

CONCLUSION

These observations demonstrate that avalanches are important agents in the downslope transfer of talus materials and indicate the possible long term effects of intense avalanche activity on talus slope development. However, despite the obvious importance of avalanche erosion at many of the sites studied it is difficult to generalise these results. The depositional evidence (Table II) clearly demonstrates the great temporal and spatial variability in the importance and intensity of avalanche activity and precludes any attempt to derive meaningful estimates of the long term rates in anything except qualitative terms. The selection of talus slopes for study in Surprise Valley is biased towards sites displaying considerable avalanche activity and, even within Surprise Valley, there are some talus slopes where avalanche activity is purely depositional and many others where it is negligible. The presence of similar landforms and deposits in the Jasper area and elsewhere in the Rockies (e.g. Gardner, 1970a) does, however, suggest that where local or regional conditions are favourable, snow avalanches play a dominant role in the development and modification of talus slopes.

Chapter 3-3

MORPHOLOGICAL CHARACTERISTICS OF ALPINE MUDFLOWS IN THE NIGEL PASS AREA.

I. F. Owens

This report refers to part of a more general study of alpine mudflows in the Nigel Pass area which includes mapping of forms associated with mudflows, investigation of sedimentary and rheological characteristics of mudflow deposits and a model study of the process of mudflowage.

The main objective of this paper is to describe the morphological properties of the mudflows studied and to compare these with examples from other parts of the world. A secondary aim is to discuss the utility of different morphological characteristics with regard to scaling; that is their usefulness as indicators of geometrical similarity over a large size range.

PREVIOUS WORK

While occurrences of alpine mudflows are not often observed, descriptions of forms associated with their occurrence are relatively frequent in the geomorphic literature. Features often associated with their initiation include moderate to steep slopes, sparse vegetation cover, intermittent water supply (often though not always from snowmelt), and presence of unconsolidated material containing abundant fines (Sharpe, 1938). While they often use old channels, mudflows may also be initiated on slopes between water courses (Sharp, 1942).

Although some alpine mudflows have resulted in extensive but relatively shallow deposits (Winder, 1965), long narrow features appear to be more common and these are often characterised by development of levees and lobes (Sharp, 1942). Usually, distinct erosional and depositional sections can be distinguished. The erosional section may be a long steep-sided gully or a bowl-shaped scar. Such features have been described for many alpine areas including the European Alps by Stiny (1910) and Tricart (1957), the Andes by Sutton (1933) and Dollfus (1960), in North America by Sharpe(1938), Sharp (1942), Fryxell and Horberg (1943), Sharp and Nobles (1953), Winder 1965), Curry (1966), Gardner (1968a), and Broscoe and Thompson (1969), the Himalayas by Conway (1893), Rickmers (1913), and Hewitt (1968), Central

Asia by Vinogradov (1969), Scandinavia by Rapp (1960a,1963) and
New Zealand by Brundall (1966).

Many of these authors have reported volumes of material
moved and in some cases, maximum thicknesses of mudflow
deposits. For example Stiny (1910) indicated maximum volumes of
$300,000$ m^3 ($10,600,000$ ft^3) for mudflows in the Alps. Dollfus
reported volumes of up to $100,000$ m^3 ($3,500,000$ ft^3). Rapp (1960a)
calculated that 10 mudflows moved a total volume of 1300 m^3
($46,000$ ft^3). In another study Rapp (1963) indicated that 26 debris
slides, which included mudflowage, moved about $300,000$ m^3
($10,600,000$ ft^3). Curry (1966) observed a mudflow in Colorado
which had a volume of 8000 m^3 ($283,000$ ft^3), while Brundall (1966)
measured deposited volumes of 40 to 3500 m^3 (1400 to $124,000$ ft^3).
However, more detailed discussion of the variation of morphological
characteristics such as length/width ratios is rare.

METHODS

Because of the interest in scaling relationships, it was
considered desirable that the mudflows studied in the field should
cover a great range of sizes. Field work consisted of levelling 19
mudflow channels and deposits, and cross-sections were measured
at several points along each flow after excavation of a trench in
depositional sections. Maps, long profiles and cross-sections
were then used to derive basic morphological variables including
slope angle (0), width (W), length (L), and depth (D) of channel or
depositional section. For each cross-section, the area of deposited
material and the area of eroded section was measured. Integration
of these values over the total mudflow length gave the volume of
deposited material (V_D) and the volume eroded (V_E). The change
from erosional to depositional character along the mudflow was
represented by an erosional-depositional index (EDI) given by:

$$EDI = \frac{A_D - A_E}{A_D + A_E}$$

where: A_D - area of deposited
material in cross-
section

A_E - area eroded.

Hence an eroded channel with no deposition would have a value of
EDI = -1.0, an entirely depositional section would have EDI = 1.0
while the division between erosional and depositional was set at
EDI = 0.0.

In order to investigate relations between morphological
variables and to allow a grouping of mudflows on a morphological
basis, a correlation of these variables was undertaken. A non-

94

parametric correlation measure, Kendall's tau, was used in this analysis.

RESULTS AND DISCUSSION

The morphological properties of the 19 mudflows studied are summarized in Table I. Although there is a wide range of sizes, the largest are small compared to the maximum sizes reported in the literature. The three largest mudflows are shown in Figure 1. The smallest mudflows examined are comparable in size to those which could be produced in laboratory experiments. The average length/width ratios indicate that the forms are long and narrow, with values varying between 6.8 and 126.0. These values are slightly higher than those found by Brundall (1966) who reported ratios ranging from 3 to 29. The mean slope angles showed only a small amount of variation. The ratio of erosional length to depositional length (L_E/L_D) indicates the predominance of either erosional or depostional sections while the average EDI can be construed as an indicator of re-use of an old channel. While it was usually possible in measurement of cross-sections to distinguish the most recent deposit from earlier ones, it was not possible to account for channel erosion caused by earlier flows. Hence a mudflow channel such as that shown in Figure 2 was probably not eroded by the recent mudflow which only partially filled the old channel. Theoretically it should not be possible for the mean EDI to be greater than 0.0. Where this does occur it must result from measurement and sampling error.

A simple Q-mode cluster analysis of the morphological characteristics indicated two major groups which are also apparent from a qualitative viewpoint.

These groups consisted of:

(1) N1, N2, N2A, N2C, N3A, N4, N5, N10, N20, N24, N30, N33

(2) N2B, N32, N34, B1, B2, B3

These two groups are basically differentiated with respect to size but several more general statements can be made about them.

The first group consists of small scale features envisaged as "modifiers" of local slope form. They commonly have straight or even convex-upward long profiles and occur on unvegetated slopes often near snow patches. Most of this type have occurred recently, several within the period of study. An example is shown in Figure 3.

TABLE I. Summary of Morphological Characteristics

No.	L (m)	D (cm)	W (cm)	V_D (m³)	V_e (m³)	O (o)	L/D	D/W	L/W	$L_E L_D$	EDI
N1	13.8	4.1	52.4	0.05	0.17	32.9	336.3	.085	26.2	0.40	-0.53
N2	66.0	24.4	298.2	9.64	11.35	34.7	271.1	.086	22.1	1.27	-0.08
N2A	34.0	19.8	167.7	4.99	2.35	36.4	171.2	.123	20.2	0.11	0.35
N2B	200.3	47.4	158.9	12.05	76.41	23.9	422.2	.295	126.0	21.16	-0.73
N2C	12.9	12.0	80.8	0.37	0.32	28.9	107.4	.151	16.0	0.35	0.06
N3A	8.4	4.2	28.2	0.001	0.004	28.6	197.3	.151	29.7	0.91	-0.45
N4	14.8	22.6	155.4	0.60	2.12	27.2	65.7	.149	9.5	2.00	-0.56
N5	20.9	13.8	130.8	1.76	0.26	32.3	152.0	.098	16.0	0.19	0.74
N10	6.0	12.6	101.7	0.34	0.14	29.7	47.4	.126	5.9	0.62	0.43
N17	17.0	18.0	155.2	1.42	1.15	23.5	94.4	.120	11.0	1.66	0.10
N20	12.4	8.5	88.6	0.86	0.80	30.4	145.5	.100	14.0	1.74	0.04
N24	24.1	15.4	155.3	8.75	4.19	27.2	156.1	.100	15.5	0.33	0.35
N30	9.1	8.9	134.7	1.22	0.88	29.7	102.3	.075	6.8	0.45	0.16
N32	134.6	61.1	450.3	90.19	131.47	31.8	220.3	.163	29.9	1.12	-0.19
N33	96.8	21.7	133.2	7.38	4.68	25.5	446.4	.174	72.7	0.62	0.22
N34	111.7	57.5	579.9	138.32	84.89	30.0	194.2	.109	19.3	3.11	0.24
B1	381.2	61.3	537.6	273.42	379.74	22.0	621.6	.125	70.9	1.14	-0.16
B2	273.5	57.8	709.6	127.84	265.91	25.3	473.5	.100	38.5	1.01	-0.35
B3	405.3	125.0	794.1	188.46	1239.81	21.4	324.2	.159	51.0	4.34	-0.74

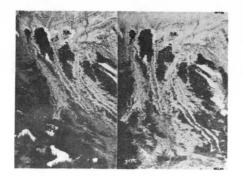

Figure 1 - Mudflows B1, B2, and B3. The relief
of the area covered is approximately
200 m. (750 ft)

Figure 2 - An erosional channel showing deposits of
a recent mudflow along the wall of the
channel. The scale is given by a small
shovel.

Figure 3 - Mudflow N2A. This flow began above
the snowpatch and continued down over
it.

The second group includes the larger features which often had a concave-upward long profile. It is thought that these mud-flows are more important as constructional agents, responsible for the fans on which most of them occur. Although commonly originating on unvegetated slopes, they often flowed into vegetated areas. Also their dates of occurrence were not as recent as those of the first type and in several cases, re-use of an erosional gully was established. Examples of each of these two types are shown in Figure 4.

Although the present study did not attempt to obtain rates of movement associated with mudflows, it is thought that both types play a significant role in current slope development. Those of the first type, though small, are quite frequent on certain slopes. They also seem to be associated with perennial snow patches and may even contribute to the development of the hollows in which these patches form. The second are thought to be important in building fan-type forms but little is known regarding the frequency of their occurrence.

The correlation matrix of morphological characteristics is shown in Table II. It is immediately apparent that the only significant correlations are those between various measures of size including the ratios L/D and L/W. However, the fact that some variables do not vary significantly with size is an important feature from a scaling viewpoint. In relation to model mudflows, the two most important are D/W and θ. The former is definitely suitable as an indicator of geometrical similarity between model and prototype.

CONCLUSIONS

Although the forms associated with alpine mudflows of the Nigel Pass area are small compared to the large features reported in the literature, the range of sizes was sufficient to allow analysis of morphological characteristics. This analysis indicated two general groups of mudflows, one consisting of small features which apparently modify local slope form above the timber line and another comprised of large features which are probably significant in constructing the fans upon which they occur. Cluster analysis indicated a set of interrelated size variables while other variables, such as depth/width ratio, did not vary with size of mudflow, and these were considered useful indicators of geometrical similarity.

TABLE II: Values of Kendall's Tau Among Morphological Variables

	L	O	V$_D$	V$_E$	EDI	D	W	D/W	L$_E$/L$_D$	L/D	L/W
L	1.00										
O	-.2749	1.00									
V$_D$	.7895	-.2281	1.00								
V$_E$	.8012	-.3099	.8480	1.00							
EDI	-.2398	.2865	-.0994	-.2515	1.00						
D	.7427	-.3216	.7427	.8012	-.1813	1.00					
W	.6725	-.2281	.7661	.8012	-.1696	.7895	1.00				
D/W	.1930	-.3567	.0760	.1579	-.2164	.2632	.0526	1.00			
L$_E$/L$_D$	.2398	-.3567	.2398	.3216	-.3918	.3333	.2865	.2515	1.00		
L/D	.6023	-.1111	.4854	.4269	-.3099	.3450	.2982	.1462	.1228	1.00	
L/W	.5906	-.1930	.4269	.4152	-.3567	.3567	.2632	.3216	.1813	.8012	1.00

For N = 19, 0.05 significance level given by   = 0.433.

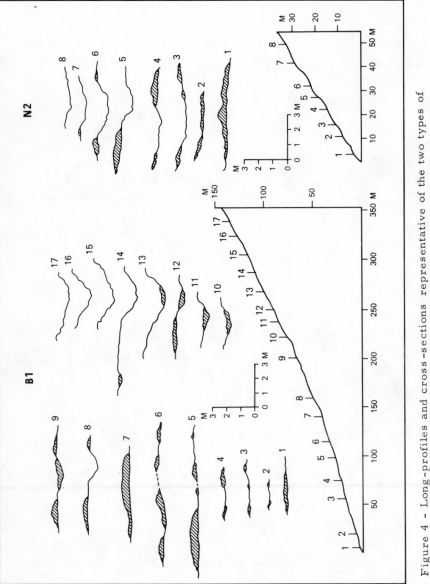

Figure 4 - Long-profiles and cross-sections representative of the two types of mudflows discussed. The shaded areas indicate deposited material.

Chapter 3-4

A PRELIMINARY STUDY OF LANDSLIDES IN THE COAST MOUNTAINS OF SOUTHWESTERN BRITISH COLUMBIA.

C. L. O'Loughlin

Landslides and related phenomena are common features on many steep, forested slopes of the Coast Mountains in south-western British Columbia. During 1970 a combined field and aerial survey of the types, extent and seriousness of landslides occurring on undisturbed forested slopes and clear-felled slopes over a selected tract of the Coast Mountains was completed. The area investigated forms an approximately 250 mi^2 (650 km^2) triangular block of steep mountain country lying between Howe Sound and Indian Arm north of the city of Vancouver (Figure 1). This paper describes the nature and results of the survey which should provide useful background information for more detailed studies of the stability of natural slopes.

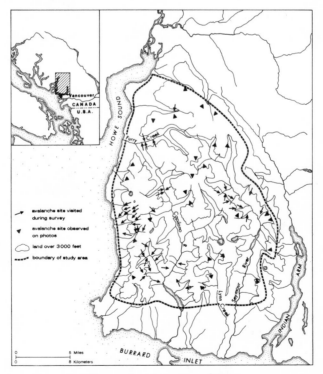

Figure 1 - Location Map

PHYSICAL SETTING OF THE STUDY AREA

Geology and Soils

Large bodies of diorite and quartz diorite associated with gneiss and migmatites dominate the bedrock geology while numerous masses of volcanic and sedimentary rock, variously interpreted as roof pendants or remnants of older terrain (Armstrong, 1965; Roddick, 1965) occur in much smaller quantities.

Pleistocene glacial ice inundated most of the area covered by the survey on at least three separate occasions. The retreating ice left widespread till deposits of variable thickness flanking the valley slopes below altitudes of 3500 ft (1070 m). Except where it is weathered the till is blue-grey in color and highly compacted. The presence of this unweathered till substratum influences the slope stability by forming an impermeable barrier to downward water flow thereby encouraging saturation of the soil mantle during storm periods. The till surface also determines the general lower limit of tree root penetration.

The topography strongly reflects the youthfulness of the mountains and the effects of the glaciations. The higher peaks, which attain a maximum altitude of 6645 ft (2025 m), are connected by uneven ridges interupted by deep transverse saddles and steep-walled narrow valleys.

Three main groups of soils are distinguishable on the valley slopes.

(a)   Soils developing on moderately to well drained sites over till or colluvium show good horizon development with incipient signs of podsolization. L, F and H horizons together are usually less than 6 in (15 cm) deep while the light yellow-brown, stoney B horizon seldom exceeds 30 in (76 cm) in thickness.

(b)   Soils developing on poorly drained sites over till are characterized by their wet condition and their strongly gleyed B horizon. Gleyed soils typify drainage depressions and seepage hollows.

(c)   Thin regosolic soils developing on bedrock usually occur on slopes over 30°.

Soils falling into categories a and b are susceptible to large scale mass movements on many steep sites whereas category c soils exhibit only occasional minor sliding. Table I presents a

summary of the physical characteristics of the B horizons of a and
b soils based on the measurement of 24 large bulk samples.

TABLE 1

	Mean Value	Std. Deviation
Moist field density	92.19 p.c.f.	9.73 p.c.f.
Dry bulk density	75.67	8.42
% gravel by weight	60.43	7.33
% sand by weight	29.63	6.93
% silt by weight	9.04	3.58
% clay by weight	0.90	0.73

Vegetation

Most slopes support a dense cover of coniferous forest
whose roots help strengthen the soil and anchor the soil to the
slopes. Western Red Cedar (Thuja plicata), Western Hemlock
(Tsuga heterophylla) and Douglas Fir (Pseudotsuga menziezii) are
the dominant canopy species on the lower slopes while Mountain
Hemlock (Tsuga mertensiana), Yellow Cedar (Chaemaecyparis
nootkatensis) and Amabilis Fir (Abies amabilis) become important
above 3000 ft (915 m).

Clear-felling has been carried out in most of the valleys
draining into Howe Sound and Burrard Inlet below altitudes of
4000 ft (1220 m).

Climate

The study area possesses a cool, moist mountain
climate notable for its heavy winter snowfalls. Seymour Falls
(el.750 ft, 230 m), in the middle Seymour valley receives an
average annual precipitation of 136 in (3455 mm), 80% of which
falls between September and March inclusive.

DATA COLLECTION

The field survey did not represent an attempt to locate
and record the details of all the mass wastage features within the
study area. Rather, most of the clear-felled slopes were visited
as well as those slopes with reasonable access (within 2 hours
climbing time from the nearest road) where slope failures were
known to occur. At each landslide site the width, depth and length
of the scar, the mean slope along each 50 ft (15 m) section of the
scar, the altitude and aspect of the scar head and the depth to
impermeable bedrock or till were measured. In addition the

character of the soil materials, the surface and subsurface hydrological conditions and the local micro-topography were recorded. Within the area of interest approximately 70% of the major slides were visited and measured.

The study was significantly aided by a stereoscopic examination of several hundred aerial photographs supplied by the Air Division, Department of Survey Services, Victoria. Five series of approximately 1:30,000 black and white panchromatic photographs taken in 1939, 1952, 1966, 1967 and 1969 and three series of 1:15,000 black and white photographs taken in 1957, 1963 and 1968 enabled the locations and approximate age of many of the major landslides to be determined.

TYPES OF MASS WASTING

During the survey landslides were not witnessed in action. Therefore the types and rates of processes responsible for a particular scar or debris accumulation could only be judged from the existing form of the feature. Nevertheless, two main types of mass wasting were distinguishable in the field.

Debris Avalanches

Debris avalanches, similar to those defined by Varnes (1958), Swanston (1967) and the features described as 'debris slides' by Rapp (1963) and recognisable by their long narrow V or crescent shaped scars up to 2000 ft (610 m) in length, are the largest mass wastage features on forested and clear-felled slopes. Apparently debris avalanches, which commonly originate in shallow drainage depressions, begin as large intact masses that suddenly break away leaving a well-marked, semicircular head scarp. These masses revert to debris avalanches as stresses cause breakdown of the soil structure. The basal sliding plane is often the upper surface of the unweathered till. High rates of movement during failure are indicated by the frequent occurrence of gravel and boulders deeply lodged in the bark and wood of tree trunks growing on the margins of avalanche scars.

On the steep slopes, particularly those underlain by shales and argillites, debris avalanches are commonly associated with logging roads.

Debris Slides

Debris slide scars are smaller in area but wider in relation to their length than debris avalanches. Often the debris

104

slide failure surface occurs within the upper soil mantle within 2 ft (0.6 m) of the surface.

Large debris flows, comparable with the debris flows described by Bishop and Stevens (1964) and dirty snow avalanches are also common features in the study area.

The remaining sections of this paper will be concerned only with debris avalanches and debris slides having surface areas greater than 1000 ft^2 (93 m^2). Examples of both types are shown in Figure 2.

SIGNIFICANCE OF LANDSLIDES IN THE COAST MOUNTAINS

A total of 77 large, recent debris avalanches and slides occur in the study area, 48 of which were investigated in the field while the remaining 29 were identified on 1968-69 aerial photographs. The general term 'landslide' is used here to include debris avalanches and slides. Table II provides an indication of the importance of landsliding in the area in terms of landslide numbers, landslide areas and weight of debris moved per square mile. The mean values of measured avalanche areas and volumes were assigned to the 29 avalanches not measured in the field while a field density of 92.2 p.c.f. (see Table I) was used for converting volumes to weights.

TABLE II

No. of slides	No. of avalanches	Mean no. of slides/ avalanches per m^2	Mean area of slides/ avalanches ft^2 per m^2	Mean weight of material moved. Tons per m^2
16	61(29)*	0.31	12,400	1,111.5

*Identified on aerial photos but not measured in field.

Compared to landslide densities (no. per unit area) in other mountainous regions (Sheng, 1966; Rapp, 1963; Dyrness. 1967 and Bishop and Stevens, 1964) the Coast Mountains densities are relatively small indicating a high degree of stability for such a steep mountain region.

The Coast Mountains landslides have a hydrological significance, not only because they are important sources of sediment but also because they form part of the surface drainage

105

Figure 2 - <u>Top left</u>. Small debris avalanche initia-
ting in a seepage hollow on a recently
clear-felled slope. <u>Top right</u>. Shallow
debris slide exposing unweathered till
surface. <u>Bottom left</u>. Debris avalanche
originating on a densely forested slope;
alder is colonising the lower portions of
the scar. <u>Bottom right</u>. Debris avalanche in second growth forest caused by
uncontrolled concentration of road drainage in the area near the scar-head.

network. Most large landslide scars possess ephemeral stream channels down the length of their longitudinal axes. In all cases investigated, however, air photos show that discernible surface drainage features did not exist on these sites prior to the time of failure. Presumably the pre-landslide downslope drainage was facilitated primarily by subsurface flow and the occurrence of an avalanche represents, therefore, an addition to the surface drainage network.

RELATIONSHIP OF LANDSLIDES TO SITE FACTORS

Thirty-one of the 48 landslides inspected in the field initiate in well marked drainage depressions or seepage hollows underlain by type b soils while 14 of the remaining 17 landslides are caused by road construction. This close association between landslides and drainage depressions supports the findings of Terzaghi (1950), Ter-Stepanian (1963) and Swanston(1970) who showed that increased pore water pressures associated with high water tables reduce the shearing resistance of soils.

Most large landslides originate on sites which fall within a relatively narrow range of slope steepness. Figure 3a shows that over 75% of the measured landslides occur on valley sides with slopes ranging from 31° to 39° inclusive. Sites with

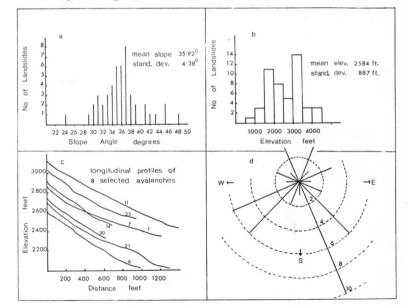

Figure 3 - (a) Frequency distribution of landslides with respect to slope. (b) Frequency distribution of landslides with respect to elevation. (c) Landslide longitudinal profiles. (d) Frequency distribution of landslides with respect to aspect.

slopes greater than 40° are usually extremely rocky and underlain by type c soils not prone to large scale failures.

The distribution of landslides with respect to altitude and aspect is shown in Figures 3b and 3c respectively. The occurrence frequency of landslides reaches a maximum between altitudes of 3000 ft and 3500 ft (915 - 1070 m), this being partly caused by the numerous slope failures related to road construction which occur above 3000 ft (915 m) in the Howe Sound area. Approximately 70% of the landslide scars examined in the field possess aspects with a southerly component.

Slope failures resulting from road construction are strongly influenced by the bedrock geology. On slopes underlain by argillites slates, sandstones and schists roadcuts have caused 9 major landslides but on slopes underlain by diorites (the situation encountered on approximately 80% of the logged-over slopes visited) only 5 major failures related to roads exist.

EFFECT OF CLEAR-CUTTING ON THE OCCURRENCE FREQUENCY OF LANDSLIDES

Croft and Adams (1950), Bishop and Stevens (1964), Dyrness (1967) and Gray (1969) have firmly established that the removal of forest may seriously increase the incidence of land-sliding on steep slopes.

Although the Coast Mountains survey revealed an increase in the frequency of landslides on clear-felled areas the extremely erratic distribution of slope failures on clear-felled and undis-turbed slopes combined with the lack of information suitable for accurately dating landslide occurrences complicated the assessment of stability changes following logging. Table III indicates the broad changes in landslide frequencies after logging on areas clear-felled between 1957 and 1968.

In order to provide more detailed information the landslide numbers and weights of landslide debris transported per mi^2 on clear-felled and on undisturbed slopes were determined for 9 subcatchment areas. The differences between the means on clear-felled and undisturbed slopes were tested with t tests. In the first set of tests all landslides were considered, in the second set only those landslides not cause by road construc-tion were included. Table IV presents the basic data and test results.

The basic data and the analysis indicates that the number of landslides per mi^2 is significantly higher on clear-felled

TABLE III

Catchment	Approx. area clear-felled between 1957 and 1968	No. of landslides 1957	No. of landslides 1968
Howe Sound Drainages	3400 acres	3	11
Capilano Catchment	371 acres	-	3
Seymour Catchment	1915 acres	-	-*

*2 small slides occur on clear-felled slopes in the mid Seymour

areas and that the construction of logging roads has a substantial influence on the occurrence of landslides.

DISCUSSION AND CONCLUSIONS

The combination of steep slopes, heavy seasonal rainfall and the presence of an impermeable till substratum predisposes many of the Coast Range slopes to catastrophic failures. The common occurrence of springs at landslide scar heads indicates that groundwater conditions play a leading role in the release of landslides.

Jackson (1966) and Swanston (1967) have shown that soils on steep slopes are most susceptible to sliding when they become completely saturated. A preliminary study of the relationship between rainfall intensities and the height of rise of the free water surface above the impermeable till or bedrock in drainage depressions within the study area using a network of piezometers yielded the relationship shown in Figure 4. This relationship provides an indication that the shallow, landslide-susceptible soils of drainage depressions will be totally saturated if the 24 hour rainfall total exceeds approximately 6 in (15 cm), an event which, according to the rainfall records in the mid Seymour valley, occurs approximately once every 2 years.

The most important human influence on landslide occurrence is the construction of logging roads. There is only limited evidence that clear-felling generally effects the incidence

TABLE IV

Catchment	No. of landslides per mi^2			Tons of landslide debris per mi^2		
	Clear-felled	Undisturbed		Clear-felled	Undisturbed	
	A	B	C	D	E	F
Furry	1.92	0.77	0.06	3,904.5	904.9	241.9
Brunswick	16.60	6.67	0.50	34,268.8	2,040.9	692.9
Magnesia	3.75	1.25	1.54	14,744.2	805.7	4,511.9
Harvey	5.71	2.86	0.50	5,468.2	1,289.1	1,959.4
Strachan	3.33	3.33	1.43	1,074.2	1,074.2	12,031.7
Sisters	1.67	1.67	0.83	572.9	572.9	1,771.6
Upper Capilano	1.88	1.88	0.38	3,363.8	3,363.8	1,051.8
Lynn	1.11	1.11	0.11	4,354.3	4,354.3	352.8
Mid Seymour	2.22	2.22	0.68	644.6	644.6	1,845.5
Means	4.24	2.42	0.67	7,599.5	1,672.3	2,717.7

A & D   All landslides considered
B & E   Road-caused landslides not considered

A vs C   t = 2.96*
B vs C   t = 2.80*   ($t_{0.01}$ = 3.17 with 8 df)
D vs F   t = 1.27 NS   ($t_{0.05}$ = 2.23 with 8 df)
E vs F   t = 0.79 NS

of debris avalanches if the effects of road construction are discontinued.

Figure 4 - Relationship between piezometric head and rainfall.

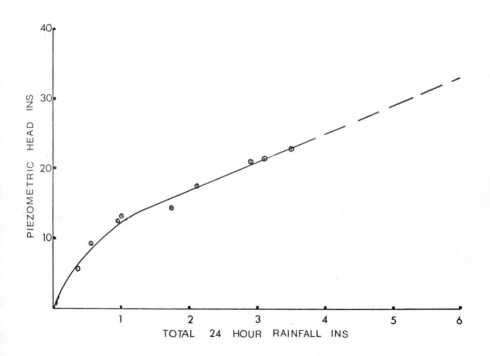

Chapter 3-5

EROSION BY OVERLAND FLOW ON AN ALPINE DEBRIS SLOPE.

P. R. Dingwall*

The process of overland, or 'pre-channel' flow
(Ellison, 1945) is one of the most ubiquitous, yet poorly understood
of all geomorphological processes on hillslopes. Notwithstanding
its common occurrence, overland flow is a difficult process to
observe under natural conditions, and it is not surprising that the
largest proportion of investigations have involved laboratory simulation or controlled experiments on agricultural plots. Prominent
among such studies are those of Ellison (1945), Smith and
Wischmeier (1962), Meyer and Monke (1965), Moldenhauer and
Koswara (1968), Bryan (1969), and Emmett (1970). Recently,
problems of monitoring sediment movement have been approached
by artificially labelling particles either radioactively (Coutts et al,
1968) or with fluorescent dyes (Young and Holt, 1968; Young and
Mutchler, 1969), while experimental plots have proved a useful
control in field studies (Haupt, 1967; Soons and Rayner, 1968;
Clauzon and Vaudour, 1969; Campbell, 1970).

Although comparatively few studies have assessed the
geomorphic role of overland flow on natural hillslopes, they have
included a wide range of morphogenetic regions. Schumm (1964)
and Leopold et al (1966) investigated slope wash in semi-arid
areas of North America; Ruxton (1967) in a selva region of New
Guinea; Young (1960) and Kirkby (1963) in the humid-temperate
realm; and Jahn (1960) on the arctic island of Spitzbergen. This
paper presents some preliminary results of a field investigation
of erosion by overland flow in a mid-latitude, alpine periglacial
realm. The results are part of a broader study of movement of
surficial material on debris slopes in the Canadian Rocky
Mountains. Debris slopes make up a large proportion of the
surface topography of the Canadian Cordillera, and function as
major sites of transport and deposition of rock debris weathered
from higher elevations. The processes of supply and mass movement of material on debris slopes have been well-documented in
the works of, among others, Rapp (1960a) and Gardner (1968a).

---

*The financial support of Dr. A. Jopling is gratefully
acknowledged.

However, such studies have focussed largely on movements of coarser components of the debris by sporadic and often catastrophic processes. Much less attention has been given to the transfer of finer fractions by slower processes affecting surficial layers of the debris. To this writer's knowledge, only Jahn (1960) and Soons and Rayner (1968) have attempted quantitative measurements of erosion by overland flow on alpine slopes.

THE FIELD AREA

The field site is a debris-covered side slope of Nigel Valley, a headwater-tributary basin of the North Saskatchewan drainage system (52°10'N, 117°05'W; Figures 1 and 2). The structural setting for Nigel Valley is the Main Ranges sub-province of the Rocky Mountain System (Price and Mountjoy, 1970). Within the valley, erosion has exposed rocks ranging in age from Cambrian to Mississippian. The debris slope is cut at a shallow angle to steeply-dipping beds of the recessive Sullivan (Upper Cambrian) Formation (Aitken and Greggs, 1967). This formation is part of a Cambrian and Ordovician succession of shaly and carbonate rocks faulted against the eastern flank of the Mount Wilson syncline, which strikes northwest and plunges to a pitch-depression at Nigel Peak (Figure 1).

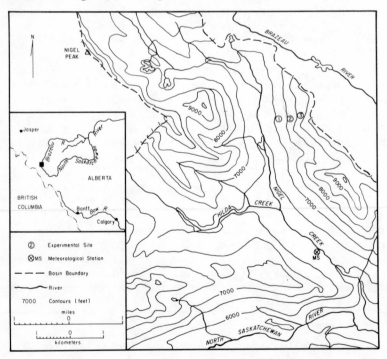

Figure 1 - Location of study area and field sites.

Figure 2 - The debris slope viewed from the west.
The numbers identify the experimental
sites.

The slope has a vertical range of 2117 ft (645 m),
extending from a local base level on the valley floor at an altitude
of 6550 ft (1996 m) and terminating on a ridge crest at 8667 ft
(2641 m). Three experimental sites selected for intensive study
are at altitudes of 7220 ft (2200 m), 7619 ft (2322 m), and 8162 ft
(2487 m).

Overall, the mean slope gradient is 22°, though the
unvegetated portion above 7172 ft (2186 m), on which this study
concentrates, has a mean gradient of 28°30'. Morphologically,
the slope is essentially simple in both cross-section and longitudinal
profile, characterized by relatively straight contours and uniformly-
sloping segments without sharp breaks of slope. The slope is
drained by two major flanking gullies which effectively isolate it
from neighbouring slopes on the valley wall. Although the basal
portion of the slope has an alpine gramineous, scrub and spruce

vegetation association, the vegetation cover of the upper portion is limited to rarely-occurring individual meadow plants.

The debris mantle comprises platey to bladed, angular fragments of calcareous shale, greyish-green in colour but weathering to olive-brown, often silty and containing fossil fragments. Common throughout the debris are smaller, grey-green, bladed to elongate, angular fragments of calcareous mudstone, weathered from thin units interbedded with the shale. The debris exhibits incipient, but distinct, horizonation which reflects mechanical sorting of material according to texture rather than the operation of truly pedogenic processes. Profiels from three excavatidns at each of the experimental sites illustrate the character of the debris (Figure 3). Individual horizons are assigned to textural classes according to the technique of Folk (1965). Although the material falls within a fairly limited range of sands and gravels, from two to three separate horizons are distinguishable in the upper 30 cm (12 in) of each profile. Values of grain-size parameters (Folk, 1965) in Table I provide a more quantitative measure of debris texture. Essentially, the debris comprises poorly or very poorly sorted sands and gravels which are fine skewed to very finely skewed and predominantly mesokurtic to leptokurtic.

FIELD METHODS

To monitor overland flow, a trough was established along the contour of each site and connected by a rubber hose to a polythene collecting tank (Figure 4). The troughs, modelled after those of Gerlach (1967), are 90 cm (36 in) long, 8 cm (3 in) wide, and 8 cm (3 in) deep. A lip protrudes 3 cm upslope immediately beneath the slope surface, and a hinged lid prevents precipitation from entering the trough directly. Sediment and runoff were collected from troughs and tanks at weekly intervals during the months of June and July, 1969 and June through August, 1970. In the laboratory the runoff was filtered and the sediment subjected to textural analysis following standard sieving and pipetting techniques.

Precipitation was measured in a direct-reading rain gauge adjacent to each trough, and in a recording rain gauge at a meteorological station on the valley floor, 4 km from the field site (Figure 1). A cylinder infiltrometer, of a design used by Hills (1970), was used to measure infiltration capacities (Figure 4). Soil moisture content was determined gravimetrically.

116

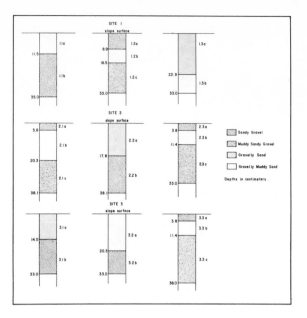

Figure 3 - Debris profiles at the experimental
sites showing textural horizonation.

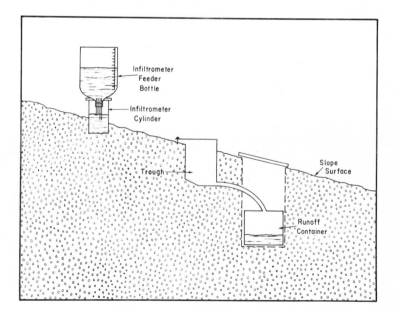

Figure 4 - Field assembly of the sediment trough,
runoff container and cylinder infiltrometer.

RESULTS AND DISCUSSION

Analysis of weekly rainfall and runoff amounts at each site, for a total period of twenty-two weeks, indicates that they are closely related. The regression of runoff on rainfall (Figure 5) has a correlation coefficient of 0.89. Of all factors controlling the ratio of runoff to rainfall, antecedent moisture appears the most important. Values designated 'wet' in Figure 5 indicate a moisture content in the surface debris of more than 10% in the previous week, and runoff at such times tends to be proportionately greater. No relationship existed between runoff and rainfall intensity. Rainfall during the study period was characteristically of low intensity, averaging 0.18 cm (0.07 in)/hour, and ranging only from 0.03 cm (0.01 in)/hour to 0.71 cm (0.28 in)/hour. In contrast, infiltration rates of the surface debris are characteristically high, and very variable even over short distances. For example, infiltration

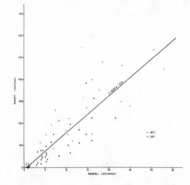

Figure 5 - Regression of weekly runoff on rainfall
amounts; r = 0.89, significant at the
0.01 level.

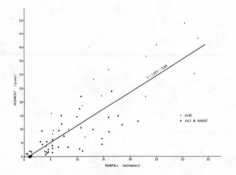

Figure 6 - Regression of weekly sediment yields
on rainfall amounts; r = 0.84, significant at the 0.01 level.

118

capacities measured at site 1 ranged from 0.18 cm (0.07 in)/hour to 0.43 cm (0.17 in)/hour, reflecting the textural variability of the debris.

A close relationship was also found between rainfall and sediment yield. The correlation coefficient for the regression of weekly sediment yields on rainfall amounts (Figure 6) is 0.84. One pattern emerging is the tendency for proportionately greater sediment yield in June. Apparently the surface debris is more susceptible to erosion when saturated, and disturbed by diurnal freezing and thawing activity accompanying ablation of the snow pack in spring. Total sediment yields of 253.0 g (8.9 oz) (site 1), 202.5 g (7.1 oz) (site 2), and 206.4 g (7.3 oz) (site 3), indicate that no one portion of the slope experiences excessively greater sediment loss than another.

A comparison of grain-size parameters of sediment eroded by overland flow (Table II) with those of surface layers of the debris at the experimental sites (Table I) shows that the eroded sediment differs mainly in being distinctly finer grained. Sorting, skewness and kurtosis characteristics are essentially comparable for the 'in-situ' and eroded sediments. Texturally, the eroded sediment strikingly resembles material comprising many of the individual horizons in the debris profiles (Figure 4). These comparisons suggest that overland flow, in addition to selectively sorting the surficial debris by washing out the finer fractions, may be responsible for much of the textural horizonation of the debris. It is notable that overland flow is competent in dislodging, if not actually transporting, material larger than sand size.

CONCLUSION

The preliminary results presented indicate that in the high alpine realm, despite a climatic regime characterised by low rainfall intensity and a regolith of high infiltration capacity, overland flow is capable of eroding measurable quantities of sediment from bare debris surfaces during summer months. Moreover, the sensitive response of runoff and sediment erosion to rainfall illustrates that here, as in other morphogenetic regions, there is a close functional relationship between meteorologic and geomorphic phenomena.

Undoubtedly, the effective operation of overland flow is limited temporally to those few months of the year when the debris is snowfree and unfrozen (four months in Nigel Valley); spatially to those surfaces unprotected by vegetation and coarse debris; and lithologically to the finer fractions of the debris. Because of these limitations, it is not expected that alpine debris slopes are dynamically adjusted in response to the overriding influence of overland flow. However, internal composition of slope debris may reflect in part its role in the selective textural sorting of slope materials.

Overland flow now warrants recognition in the spectrum of geomorphic processes effecting the translocation of debris on alpine valley-side slopes. Determination of its relative effectiveness as a geomorphic agent in the evolution of alpine slopes awaits further quantitative investigation of slope processes.

TABLE I: Grain-size characteristics of the debris at the experimental sites. Horizon designations refer to those illustrated in Figure 3.

Site	Profile	Grain-size parameters			
		Mz (ø)	O_I (ø)	Sk_I	K_g
1	1.1a	- 0.13	3.57	0.21	1.55
	1.1b	- 2.50	3.21	0.74	0.93
	1.2a	- 3.99	2.34	0.57	1.15
	1.2b	+ 0.53	3.38	0.26	0.95
	1.2c	- 1.16	3.98	0.50	0.91
	1.3a	+ 0.23	2.36	0.39	1.58
	1.3b	+ 0.58	3.49	0.38	1.36
2	2.1a	- 3.96	2.11	0.56	1.30
	2.1b	+ 0.25	2.77	0.41	1.60
	2.1c	- 1.14	3.58	0.23	0.73
	2.2a	+ 0.16	2.57	0.35	1.56
	2.2b	- 3.13	2.47	0.53	1.77
	2.3a	- 3.77	1.76	0.68	1.45
	2.3b	+ 0.65	2.84	0.28	1.07
	2.3c	- 1.17	3.38	0.45	0.93
3	3.1a	+ 0.30	2.57	0.26	1.71
	3.1b	- 2.56	2.65	0.46	0.88
	3.2a	+ 0.45	2.85	0.32	1.55
	3.2b	- 3.29	2.39	0.88	0.97
	3.3a	- 3.78	1.74	0.27	1.22
	3.3b	+ 0.34	2.51	0.39	1.56
	3 3c	- 3.32	2.47	0.80	1.13

TABLE II: Grain-size characteristics of sediment eroded by overland flow.

Site	Date	Grain-size parameters				Textural Class
		Mz (ø)	O_I (ø)	Sk_I	K_G	
1	1969	+ 0.90	2.81	0.44	1.06	muddy sand
	1970	- 0.65	2.45	0.17	1.00	gravelly sand
2	1969	+ 0.63	2.67	0.41	1.24	muddy sand
	1970	+ 0.64	3.04	0.43	1.41	gravelly muddy sand
3	1969	+ 0.12	2.45	0.40	1.04	gravelly muddy sand
	1970	+ 0.18	2.64	0.20	1.18	gravelly muddy sand

120

Chapter 3-6

INTERFLOW IN THE MOUNTAINOUS FOREST SOILS
OF COASTAL BRITISH COLUMBIA.

T. W. Chamberlin*

Interflow is the process of water movement parallel to
the soil surface caused by boundary conditions sufficiently restric-
tive to prevent normal vertical infiltration and percolation to a
water table. Mass movements in S. E. Alaska (Bishop and
Stevens, 1964), in the West Kootenay Region of British Columbia
(Chamberlin and Jeffrey, 1967), and in the Coast Mountains of
British Columbia (O'Loughlin, 1971) have been described with
seepage zones located in headwall sites. This has led to the
hypothesis that interflow may be an important process in the
creation of unstable conditions.

From the viewpoint of hydrology, interflow in the form
of subsurface stormflow has been invoked for some time as the
dominant process contributing to quick stream response following
precipitation events in forested regions (Nutter, 1969; Whipkey,
1969; Hursh, 1944). The development of the variable source area
concept (Betson and Marius, 1969) has led to further questions
about the types of soils which in a given watershed transmit
relatively high water fluxes.

Understanding of the mechanism of water transmission
and retention in forest soils has been limited by their complexity
relative to agricultural soils, and by their internal heterogeneity.
Root channels (Gaiser, 1952), basal pipes (Weyman, 1970; Il'in,
1970), "macropores" from root and animal activity (Tsukamoto,
1961) and anisotropic conductivity fields (Liakopoulos, 1965;
Zaslavsky and Ragowski, 1969) have been invoked to provide the
necessary rapid transmission of stormflow runoff. Whipkey (1969)
has demonstrated that water is in fact passed through unwetted
soils enroute to draining areas.

Despite observations of rapid stormflow drainage from
areas without overland flow, it has also been shown that base flow
is sustained by continuous unsaturated flow from the entire soil

*The financial support of the Faculty of Forestry,
University of British Columbia is gratefully acknowledged.

121

column (Hewlett, 1961; Hewlett and Hibbert, 1967; Horton and Hawkins, 1965). Hence, within the forest soils mentioned it appears that the normal infiltration-percolation-groundwater sequence of classical soil physics is initially bypassed, but not excluded from longer term response.

These observations and hypotheses have led to the present study, intended to determine in situ soil water conditions in the shallow coastal mountain soils of British Columbia.

THEORY OF SOIL WATER MOVEMENT

The generalized flow equation (Elrick and Aalders, 1968)

$$\frac{\partial w}{\partial t} = \nabla \cdot \left[K(W) \nabla \psi \right]$$

where w = water content, t = time, k(w) = hydraulic conductivity, and ψ = total water potential combines a statement of continuity with Darcy's Law. It implies that changes in the water content of a soil are due to the gradient of a continuous potential field. Water potential measurements, as with a tensiometer, together with water flux define the hydraulic conductivity of the soil domain.

We ask the question, do points in the drainage sequence exist when flow is not Darcian, i.e., when flux rates are not determined by the potential field of the soil mass through which the water is moving.

IN SITU MEASUREMENTS OF SOIL WATER POTENTIAL

The experimental site (located in the Seymour River drainage near Vancouver, B. C.) is in a mature Western Hemlock - Red Cedar forest at 700 m (2300 ft) on a 30° slope. Soil depth averages 1 m (3 ft) over a quartz-diorite bedrock. The area has been extensively glaciated and was last exposed about 10,000 years ago. Present soils are humic to orthohumic podsols (Canadian Soil Classification System) with thick organic layers (10 - 30 cm; 4 - 12 in), a well developed A_e horizon, and B horizons ranging from 0 to 1 m (0 to 3 ft).

Root development in the profile is extensive. Roots, dead roots, logs, and other old wood may constitute 50% of the organic and A horizons (20 - 50 cm; 8 - 20 in). Live roots penetrate to and along weathered bedrock surfaces (1 - 1.5 m; 3 - 5 ft). Forest floor micromorphology includes large voids extending up to 1 m (3 ft), particularly under large roots and stumps.

Precipitation over the previous 12 months was 368 cm (145 in) at the 640 m (2100 ft) level.

Surface drainage is evidenced in small sub-parallel to dendritic ephemeral channels, spaced at about 10 m intervals, and controlled by bedrock morphology, large trees, and rock outcrops. At times exposed and at times underground, these channels may be considered either as large soil features or as small streams. Water in these channels is the first evidence of true interflow, since it implies either that the underlying material is saturated or that adjacent soils are releasing free water laterally into the channel.

PROCEDURE

A 4 m^2 (43 ft^2) grid of 18 low impedence, rapid response tensiometers was located at 10 (4), 30 (12), 70 (28), and 100 cm (40 in) depths at 5 stations to measure 3-dimensional variation in water potential. These depths correspond approximately to the organic A_1, B, and basal soil layers. Osmotic and thermally induced flow was assumed negligible. Response to natural and simulated rainfall was read on manometers located downslope and plotted against time and precipitation (Figure 1). In addition, equi-potential contour plots were made of vertical transects oriented up slope (y-z plane) and across slope (x-z plane) to establish potential gradient directions and magnitudes (Figure 2).

Water inputs were of two types:

1.   Irrigation at 1.7 cm (0.7 in)/hr. for 3 days following a 2 week drainage period.

2.   A precipitation event (following 2 days drainage) at .02 to .04 cm (0.008 to 0.017 in)/hr. for 6 hours with a 30 min. irrigation at hour 4 of 3.5 cm (1.38 in)/hr. to introduce a measurable pulse into the system.

It was assumed that following the wetting period of 3 days the soil-water system would be at a "wet" equilibrium state.

RESULTS (1)

Figure 2 is an equi-potential contour map of the y-z plane at "wet" equilibrium following 2 days of irrigation. Equivalent plots of the x-z plane indicate that non-vertical fluxes are dominantly in the y-z plane, or up and down slope. Since the system is at equilibrium, and since flow lines are in the y-z plane, we make the assumption that input flux rate (1.7 cm (0.7 in)/hr.)

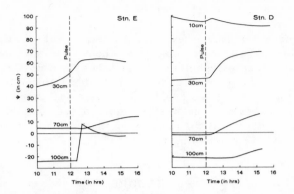

Figure 1 - Response to irrigation pulse during rainfall by depth.

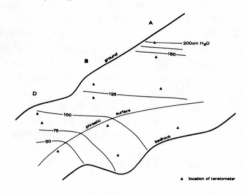

Figure 2 - Potential field distribution at "wet"
equilibrium (in cm H_2O)

is equal to the unsaturated flux rate in the soil. Estimating the
unsaturated hydraulic conductivity by applying Darcy's Law in the
form of k(w) = flux/potential gradient, and assuming that flow is
dominantly vertical (Figure 2; unsaturated zone), yields conductivities ranging from 1.7 cm (0.7 in)/hr. in the organic
horizon to 0.3 cm (0.012 in)/hr. in the B horizon.

A similar analysis can be applied to the saturated zone
if a flux rate can be estimated. Irrigation is applied upslope from
Stn. D for a distance of 4 m (13 ft). Assuming that the total of this
flow drains through the 30 cm (12 in) of free water under Stn. D,
then the saturated flux rate must be about 13 times the input rate,
or about 22 cm (8.7 in)/hr. Combined with the potential gradient
just under the phreatic surface, this yields a saturated conductivity
of about 35 cm (13.8 in)/hr.

RESULTS (2)

Response time variation between stations and depths was large, but some generalizations can be made.

Basal and 70 cm (28 in) levels responded either very slowly or very rapidly. At some stations the 70 cm (28 in) response began before the basal response, while at others, after. On the assumption that flow followed the shortest route from surface to basal layer (100 cm : 40 in), total profile conductivities ranged from 67 to 200 cm (26 to 80 in)/hr.

Response at 30 cm (12 in) was rapid, appearing in each case in less than 30 min. This seems reasonable, since the combined organic and A_e horizons, both very permeable, averaged about 20 cm.

Organic layer response (10 cm : 4 in) was immediate. Equilibrium wet state was reached within minutes of initial pulse. In most cases the 4 hours of natural rainfall had already penetrated to 10 cm (4 in). In no case had response been observed at 30 cm (12 in).

CONCLUSIONS

The organic horizon easily transmits high intensity inputs (1.7 cm (0.7 in)/hrs.). This is further supported by the complete absence of surface runoff during treatment.

At equilibrium "wet" state the saturated basal zones have a Darcy conductivity of about 35 cm (13.8 in)/hr., while conductivities in the unsaturated B horizon range from 0.3 - 1.7 cm (0.12 - 0.7 in)/hr. But total profile response reached 200 cm (80 in)/hr.

Logically, routes of drainage must exist which are open between organic layer voids and basal zones. Initial B horizon wetting is thus from both top and bottom.

Since basal zones drain rapidly and contain live roots and oxidized parent material, a true water table does not exist.

If the generalized flow equation is to be used in conductivity or water balance determination, flux heterogeneity must be estimated for meaningful results.

Interflow in the study site is dominantly in the form of saturated flow over shallow bedrock, aided by rapid transmission through intervening soil. Unsaturated flow above the phreatic surface is dominantly vertical.

DISCUSSION

The hydrologic properties of coastal British Columbia soils are dominated by the vegetation of the mature forest. With respect to their drainage properties, we suggest that such forest soils may be usefully classified as one of the following two types:

A <u>closed</u> soil is one in which water passes to a water table or stream by means of continuous unsaturated flow. Flow is controlled by the total water potential of the soil en masse, and flux densities are reasonably homogeneous. Soils described by Hewlett (1961) and Hewlett and Hibbert (1967) are of this type, with long term base flow derived from the entire soil mass. Stormflow in a closed soil is initiated when zones of saturation become, in effect, ephemeral streams.

An <u>open</u> soil is one in which a large quntity of water passes to the water table or stream channel through pathways which circumvent most of the soil mass. Such pathways must be sufficiently interconnected to rapidly transmit large precipitation inputs, and must be continuous with the soil surface to contact free water before it is absorbed into the soil matrix. It seems probable that tree roots are the primary mechanism for forming an open soil.

Theoretically, open and closed soils are identical since physical obstructions or voids may be viewed as elements of the soil matrix whose hydraulic condictivities are either very small or very large. We have asked whether it is the case that such anomalies are sufficiently common to modify the classical picture of soil water movement with respect to runoff generation and soil stability.

In our watershed, this seems to be so; slopes contain dominantly open soils, whereas ledges and slump blocks are closed, contain boggy vegetation, and drain slowly throughout the year.

We hypothesize that root development relative to soil depth is the most important of the soil forming factors with respect to the degree of "openness" of a soil. If roots penetrate to the first impermeable layer, it is likely that an open soil will develop; if not, the intervening soil will homogenize flux densities and close the drainage pattern.

126

An open soil explains the very flashy response of coastal streams to precipitation events. Stormflow is that component of runoff which is transmitted by saturated flow through anomalous zones of the soil. Baseflow is then supplied by unsaturated flow from remaining volumes at rates and quantities determined by antecedent soil moisture and the degree to which a given precipitation event has saturated the entire profile.

In the context of the variable source area concept, open and closed soils may serve as the two types of source areas which determine the hydrologic response of a given watershed. A partition might be made through soil depth-vegetation mapping.

Soil stability is influenced, through cohesion and hydraulic pressure, by the degree of wetness of a block of soil. O'Loughlin has noted that Coast Mountain soils are amazingly stable for their slopes and degree of denudation after logging. Bishop and Stevens demonstrated a decrease in stability several years following logging and attributed it to a reduction in soil strength due to the decay of tree roots.

An alternative and complementary hypothesis is that the stability of steep mountain soils is related to their ability to quickly drain large volumes of water (over 375 cm (148 in)/yr.) without saturating the entire soil mass. Instability would then follow vegetation removal if root disintegration caused long term collapse of voids in soil structure which hitherto had allowed rapid drainage.

This approach might explain mass movements in logged areas more easily by permitting inferences to be drawn from forest cutting to the stability equation through more than the cohesion term and the loss of root strengths. Increased water contents might also influence cohesion, and exert positive hydraulic pressures.

We conclude that land use in general will change the hydrology of a watershed in direct proportion to the area of open soils in the watershed, and the degree to which it affects this openness. A productive avenue for research in land use hydrology will be the quantification of the effects of various land use influences on soil structures, not only at the surface, but also at shallow depths, and over extended time periods.

SECTION   FOUR

FLUVIAL   PROCESSES   AND   MORPHOLOGY

Chapter 4-1

HYDRAULIC PERFORMANCE OF STEEP NATURAL CHANNELS.

Rolf Kellerhals

Flow in certain steep, natural channels is characterized by frequent hydraulic jumps, irregular and ill defined flow areas, large velocity fluctuations and entrainment of air into the flowing water. The size of individual roughness elements may be of the same order as the depth of flow, or even comparable to the width of the channel (Figure 1). Peterson and Mohanty (1960) introduced the very descriptive term "tumbling flow" to characterize this flow regime.

Tumbling flow has been the object of several recent investigations (Peterson and Mohanty, 1960; Morris, 1968; Scheuerlein, 1968; Judd and Peterson, 1969). The emphasis has been on engineering hydraulic aspects of this flow regime, with two of the major studies (Morris, 1968; Scheuerlein, 1968) dealing with the design of steep highway drainage ditches. Flow formulas have been developed which permit reasonable estimates of mean velocity and mean depth if discharge, slope, channel cross-section and the nature of the roughness elements are known.

Besides affecting certain engineering design problems, tumbling flow also plays an important role in the hydrologic performance of steep basins, since most of the channel flow in mountainous areas takes place in the tumbling regime. From the hydrologic point of view the results of the above-mentioned studies are inadequate because the flow formulas require information about channel roughness and channel shape which is virtually unobtainable in most cases.

The objective of this study was to approach the hydraulics of tumbling flow from a purely hydrologic point of view. A priori it appeared possible to overcome the difficulties associated with the use of customary flow formulas by making full use of the fact that most tumbling flow channels which are of hydrologic interest are also self-formed through degradation into debris on the valley floor. The size, shape and roughness of the channel at a given point should therefore be closely related to the discharge regime imposed from upstream and to the channel slope. The latter is available on topographic maps and the former can be estimated roughly from

Figure 1 - Two typical tumbling flow channels:
(a) Phyllis Creek, near Britannia, B.C.,
view downstream.
(b) Brockton Creek, Mt. Seymour
Park, Vancouver, B.C., view upstream.

meteorologic and map information. The hydrologic approach also permits the use of simpler flow formulas than those needed in engineering design problems, since local flow velocities or the cross-sectional parameters are irrelevant, steady flow being adequately defined by a relation between storage per unit length, A, (cross-sectional area) and discharge, Q: $A = f(Q)$.

Besides a steady flow formula, a hydrologic model of channel flow also requires unsteady flow equations suitable for routing flood hydrographs through a channel reach. Here the a priori expectation was that tumbling flow channels should behave as kinematic flow systems (Lighthill and Whitham, 1955). In general, kinematic waves arise in one-dimensional flows if, at every location X, there exists a unique function between the quantity per unit time (Q, in the case of a river) and the quantity per unit length (A). Certain traffic flows and the flow in steep river reaches (not tumbling) are known to be kinematic.

FIELD PROGRAM

To test the above-mentioned assumptions regarding steady and unsteady flow, an extensive program of field measurements was carried out during 1967 and 1968, mainly in the Coast Mountains north of Vancouver, British Columbia. Twelve test reaches, covering a wide range of width 2.9 ft (0.89 m) to 42 ft (12.8 m) and slope (0.03 to 0.35; 1°43' to 19°18') were selected. To permit unsteady flow tests all reaches had to contain upstream lakes. All reaches were surveyed for thalweg length, slope, and width between the apparent high-water marks.

For each reach, five to ten points on the steady flow function $A = f(Q)$ were obtained with the aid of tracer tests (Church and Kellerhals, 1970). If a slug of tracer of mass, M, is injected into a stream of constant but unknown discharge, Q, and the variation of tracer concentration, C(t), is observed at a location sufficiently far downstream to permit the assumption of almost complete lateral and vertical mixing, then the discharge is given by the formula:

$$Q = \frac{M}{\int_{t_s}^{t_e} C \, dt} \tag{1}$$

in which t_s = arrival time of the tracer and t_e = the time at which all the tracer has passed the downstream location.

If the tracer is distributed rapidly across the stream and the total test reach is much larger than this mixing length, then

one obtains the mean travel time of the stream water, T, between
the point of injection and the sampling point as

$$ T = \frac{\int_{t_s}^{t_e} C \, dt}{\int_{t_s}^{t_e} \frac{C}{t} \, dt} \tag{2} $$

By inserting these simultaneous T and Q values into the equation of
continuity Q = A L/T (in which L is the length of the reach) one can
compute A, and then plot one point of the steady flow function A =
f(Q).

The unsteady flow tests consisted of creating small,
sudden changes in discharge by obstructing or deepening the upstream lake outlets. At the end points of the test reaches, which
were selected to coincide with stable pools, the passage of the
surges was observed as water level changes. Linearly damped
manual and recording gauges were used, which could be read to
$\pm$ 0.001 ft ($\pm$ 0.3 mm). This was adequate resolution as the total
level change of a test was generally in the order of $\pm$ 0.05 ft
($\pm$ 15 mm). The design of the equipment and the method used for
removing the effect of linear damping from the record are
described in Church and Kellerhals (1970). On the basis of the
stage-discharge curves obtained in the course of the tracer tests,
the adjusted stage readings could be converted to hydrographs
(time vs. discharge). Figure 2 shows the results of 3 surge tests.

The final field data consist of 150 tracer tests and 22
surge tests (Kellerhals, 1969, 1970).

ANALYSIS OF RESULTS

Steady Flow

Various simple functional forms of the steady flow
equation A = f(Q) were fitted to the best data sets. Only experimental equations of the form

$$ A = aQ^b \tag{3} $$

gave consistently good fits. A typical example is shown in Figure
3. The value of the exponent b was found to be in agreement with
accepted hydraulic principles. For a broad channel with a rough
boundary and uniform flow (not tumbling), the expected value of b
is 0.6 (Manning's Equation), while for a cascade of broad pools

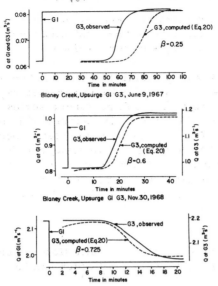

Blaney Creek, Upsurge GI G3, June 9,1967

Blaney Creek, Upsurge GI G3, Nov.30,1968

Blaney Creek, Downsurge GI G3, March 5,1968

Figure 2 - Three typical surge tests on Blaney
Creek, between gauges 1 and 2. (from
Kellerhals, 1970)

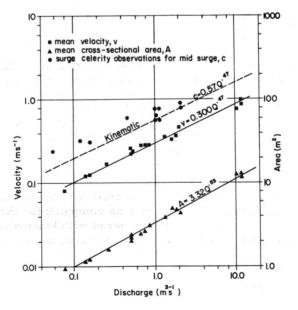

- ■ mean velocity, v
- ▲ mean cross-sectional area, A
- • surge celerity observations for mid surge, c

Figure 3 - Hydraulic measurements on the reach
"Blaney Creek, gauge 3 - gauge 5".
(from Kellerhals, 1970)

controlled by parabolic weirs the value for b is 0.29. All values observed in the field fell between these extremes with the smaller and steeper reaches showing smaller b values.

Equation 3 is only useful if the parameters a and b can be predicted from readily available basin parameters, as it would be unreasonable to expect anyone to perform a series of tracer tests on every stream of interest. The sample of 12 test reaches was too small to examine the multivariate relation between basin parameters, such as slope and drainage area, and the parameters a and b. Day (1970) collected data for another 11 reaches and was then able to develop practical estimating equations for a and b. Day's study is discussed elsewhere in this volume.

Kinematic Waves

Wave propagation in a kinematic flow system is governed by the equation of continuity, which can be written in differential form as

$$\frac{\partial A}{\partial t} + \frac{\partial A}{\partial x} = 0 \tag{4}$$

or alternatively

$$\frac{\partial A}{\partial t} + \frac{\partial Q}{\partial A}\frac{\partial A}{\partial x} = 0 \tag{5}$$

This latter form is also a wave equation with $\partial Q/\partial A$ having the dimensions of a velocity. Equation 5 states than an observer moving downstream along a river at a speed $\partial Q/\partial A$ will observe steady flow, even though flood waves may be passing down the river. Kinematic waves are therefore non-dispersive and, since $\partial Q/\partial A$ increases with increasing discharge, all positive wave fronts should steepen continuously and eventually form bores.

In order to compare these theoretically based statements with field evidence, the wave velocities as computed for the mid-points of up and down-surges were compared with kinematic wave velocities. According to Equation 3 the kinematic wave velocity $c = \partial Q/\partial A$ is

$$c = \frac{1}{a\,b} Q^{1-b} \tag{6}$$

Figure 3 shows both the observed and the computed

kinematic velocities. The agreement was generally good, although the observed velocities exceeded the kinematic velocity considerably at low stages. The main mechanism governing flood wave movement is certainly kinematic, but, contrary to truly kinematic waves, both positive and negative wave fronts show a clear tendency towards flattening. This indicates that a dispersive term should be added to Equation 5.

Since tumbling flow is characterized by frequent hydraulic jumps, separated by deeper, pool-like channel segments, it seemed reasonable to replace the (kinematic) assumption that the flow system is governed by a unique A-Q function anywhere along its length with the alternate assumption that the flow system consists of a series of short storage elements, each of which is governed by a unique A-Q relation at its outlet.

Under these conditions, Equation 5 takes the following form

$$\frac{\partial A}{\partial t} + c\frac{\partial A}{\partial x} = -\beta W_D \frac{\partial^2 A}{\partial x \partial t} \tag{7}$$

in which W_D is the channel width between high water marks and β is a dimensionless coefficient which remains to be determined. An analytical solution of Equation 6 could be obtained for the relatively simple initial and boundary conditions of the surge tests (small, step-like changes in Q superimposed on a steady state). The details of the solution are discussed in Kellerhals (1969). The solution for a step-like surge, during which A is increased from A_o to $(1 + \alpha) A_o$, with $\alpha \ll 1$, is

$$A(\ell, t) = \frac{A_o}{\beta W_D} \int_0^\ell \frac{\beta W_D}{4\pi\sqrt{ct(\ell-x)}} \exp\left(\frac{2\sqrt{ct(\ell-x)}-\ell-ct+x}{\beta W_D}\right) dx$$

$$+ \frac{2(1+\alpha)A_o c\ell}{\beta^2 W_D^2} \int_0^t \sqrt{\frac{\beta W_d}{4\pi\sqrt{c\ell(t-\tau)}}} \exp\left(\frac{2\sqrt{c(t-\tau)}-\ell-ct+c\tau}{W_D}\right) d\tau \tag{8}$$

τ is a dummy time variable and ℓ is the length of the reach. This equation was evaluated numerically and fitted to the surge data by varying β until good fits were obtained. Replacing the dispersion coefficient βW_D with the estimated actual water surface width, W_s, appeared to give consistently good fits. Figure

2 compares 3 sets of field data with their computed equivalent, using estimates of W_s as the dispersion coefficient.

A Practical Routing Model

As a computationally simpler alternative to Equation 8 a further routing model was developed, in which the channel is replaced by a cascade of pairs of non-linear reservoirs (for dispersion of waves) and of truly kinematic channel segments (for the downstream progression of waves).

The basic steady flow equation (Equation 3) can be satisfied physically with either an inclined rough channel with the appropriate roughness elements, or with a smooth, almost horizontal reservoir-like channel, controlled at the downstream end by a weir of the appropriate shape. To simplify computations, the wave velocity of the pools was assumed to be infinite. Figure 4 shows the model in schematic form and illustrates the meaning of the 2 free parameters, n and σ . Rules for evaluating these parameters and the computational procedures for routing flow through this model are discussed in Kellerhals (1969). The model is much more versatile than Equation 8 and appears to provide equally good fits.

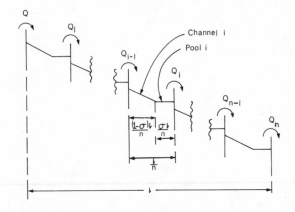

Figure 4 - Schematic diagram of the non-linear routing model.

CONCLUSIONS

Firstly, it has been shown that steady tumbling flow in steep natural channels can be described by an exponential flow formula in which the effects of the channel boundary and of channel slope are implicit, and the parameters of this flow formula can be estimated from readily available basin data on the basis of formulas developed by Day (1970). Secondly, flood waves propagate essentially as kinematic waves but the addition of a dispersion term to the wave equation improves the fit considerably. Water surface width gives a good estimate of the dispersion coefficient, and for practical flood routing purposes the channels can be replaced by a cascade of pairs of non-linear storage elements and truly kinematic channel segments. Thirdly, the channel reaches tested show no tendency towards linear response.

Chapter 4-2

THE CHANNEL GEOMETRY OF MOUNTAIN STREAMS.

Terry J. Day[*]

Steady flow parameters of steep, natural channels are related to readily available channel and basin parameters. The objectives of this study are: (1) to establish the relations between steady flow parameters and channel dimensions; (2) to establish the relations between basin and channel characteristics to permit substitution of basin properties in (1); and, (3) to investigate regional climatic effects on these relations.

The channel networks studied have developed in valleys whose longitudinal slopes are relict glacial features. In basins developed by stream action alone, the channel slopes can be related to discharge and drainage area (Wolman, 1955; and Miller, 1958). However, in basins modified by glacial action, channel slopes may be considered as independent of both discharge and drainage area.

As these channels are self-formed by degradation into glacial debris, channel width is closely related to the upstream discharge regime. As discharges for constant frequencies are proportional to basin area (Miller, 1958; and Gann, 1969), close relations between channel width and contributing drainage area are expected. The relations between channel and basin dimensions can be considered as follows:

$$W_D = f\left(\left|\frac{Q_D}{DA}\right|, S\right) \tag{1}$$

where W_D is the channel width; DA, the contributing drainage area; Q_D, the formative discharge; and S, channel slope. Several independent variables may be missing from this equation (e.g., time distribution of discharge, sediment supply); however, the dominant independent variables are included. The effect of vegetation and log jams, an important factor in streams with widths

---

*The financial support of the Departments of Geography and Civil Engineering at the University of British Columbia is gratefully acknowledged.

141

less than 15 m (50 ft), because of an obvious measuring difficulty, is ignored. Channel roughness is also ignored because its evaluation necessitates extensive, impractical field work. It is hoped that the effect of these missing variables is either implicit or of minor importance.

Equation 1, represents an attempt to establish relations between channel and basin dimensions in terms of readily available data on channel slope, channel width and drainage area, which can be collected with a minimum of field work or from topographic maps and aerial photographs.

Work by Leopold and Maddock (1953) indicated that, for steady flow conditions in natural channels, the elements of the continuity equation, $Q = Av_m$, where A is the flow area and v_m the mean velocity, vary with discharge, Q, as simple power functions at a given river cross-section. The functions of interest are:

$$A = a_A Q^{b_A} \qquad (2)$$

$$v_m = a_v Q^{b_v} \qquad (3)$$

Flow area is used instead of the usual separate solutions for width and depth because the irregular nature of the channel cross-section makes determination of these variables arbitrary and meaningless.

It is unnecessary to calculate (or to predict) both equations 2 and 3 as:

$$a_A \cdot a_v = 1$$

$$b_A + b_v = 1$$

Since water storage per unit length of channel is the parameter of most hydrologic significance, the relations between the constants in equation 2 and the channel and basin dimensions are to be investigated. As these constants can be considered results of the interaction between the hydrologic and morphologic characteristics of the channel the following formal relations can be expected:

$$\begin{vmatrix} a_A \\ b_A \end{vmatrix} = f(\begin{vmatrix} Q_D \\ DA \\ W_D \end{vmatrix}, S) \qquad (4)$$

142

FIELD PROGRAM

Objectives

This project was originally designed to supplement a concurrent research program on runoff concentration in steep channel networks undertaken by Kellerhals (1969, 1970) by providing flow data from a wider range of channels and basins. Kellerhals' data encompass 12 test reaches on four streams (Brockton, Blaney, Placid and Phyllis) in the southern Coast Mountains of British Columbia. A further five reaches were selected in the Coast Mountains on Slesse, Phyllis and Furry Creeks, while six reaches were selected from Ashnola River Basin in the Cascade Mountains of drier, south-central British Columbia. These six reaches were chosen to provide information concerning climatic influences on the channel forming processes. Table I lists the sites along with the relevant channel and basin parameters.

Field Methods

The two channel dimensions to be measured in the field, width and slope, were determined simultaneously by chaining and hand levelling along the reach at either 15 or 30 m (50 or 100 ft) intervals, depending on the length of the reach. Channel widths were measured between high water marks, usually fairly well defined by a vegetation trimline. Operator error is not thought to have amounted to more than 10%. Slope (S) was calculated as drop over length, or sin θ.

Drainage areas were planimetered from 1:50,000 scale maps except in cases where the basin bordered on the United States; here smaller scale American maps were used.

Stream discharges were calculated by the "relative salt dilution" method (see Church and Kellerhals, 1970, for a recent critique of the method). The high degree of turbulence in mountain channels makes this method more practical than most others.

Flow equations for the test reaches were established from linear regression of the logarithms of A and Q of equation 2. Table II lists the derived constants. The standard error of estimate varied from 1% to 13.2%. All equations explain at least 98% of the data variance; the unexplained variance may be due either to measurement errors or to minor changes in the channel cross-section.

TABLE 1

CHANNEL DATA

Creek	Location (Mid-reach)	Reach (going down stream)	Slope	Drainage Area (km^2)	Mean Width (m)	Predicted Channel Width (m) (Eq. 5)
Brockton	Lo: 122° 56' Lat: 49° 23'	1-2	.074	0.9	0.72	0.9
		2-3	.349	1.0	0.09	1.0
Placid	Lo: 122° 34' Lat: 49° 18.5'	1-2	.083	2.8	0.6	2.8
		2-3	.036	3.2	1.2	4.0
		3.4	.034	7.0	2.6	6.1
Blaney	Lo: 122° 34.5' Lat: 49° 17'	1.3	.047	12.8	7.4	10.5
		3.5	.039	11.1	7.7	10.7
		5.4	.095	12.9	7.9	10.9
Phyllis	Lo: 123° 11' Lat: 49° 34'	1-2	.031	11.5	8.7	11.4
		2-3	.049	12.6	10.4	12.6
		3-4	.064	12.6	11.0	12.9
		4-6	.099	12.3	11.3	13.2
		5	.219	14.0	11.8	13.4
Furry	Lo: 120° 12' Lat: 40° 36'		.129	20.3	39.0	25.2
Slesse	Lo: 121° 38' Lat: 49° 91'	1	.034	19.5	105.1	
	Lo: 121° 38' Lat: 49° 91'	2	.043	22.8	110.4	
	Lo: 121° 39' Lat: 40° 02'	3	.034	26.7	126.0	
Juniper	Lo: 120° 01' Lat: 49° 06'		.134	6.0	21.8	6.4
Ewart	Lo: 120° 02' Lat: 49° 08'	1	.035	16.4	90.8	13.4
	Lo: 120° 02' Lat: 49° 08'	2	.041	14.2	95.8	13.9
Ashnola	Lo: 120° 11' Lat: 49° 10'	1	.010	21.1	221.5	21.3
	Lo: 120° 10' Lat: 49° 10'	2	.026	28.2	408.5	29.3
	Lo: 120° 10' Lat: 49° 10'	3	.035	22.1	409.5	

144

Basin and Channel Characteristics

The form of Equation 1 was investigated statistically using drainage area (DA) and slope (S) as the independent variables. The equation is not free of climatic influence, since for a given formative discharge and channel width, larger drainage areas are required in regions of lower precipitation. The constants of this equation will reflect this climatic effect.

The best fitting equations were supplied by multiple regression analysis on the logarithmically transformed data. As S is non-significant at the 5% level, simple linear regressions are adequate:

$$W_c = 3.7 \, DA^{0.53} \tag{5a}$$

$$W_a = 1.3 \, DA^{0.52} \tag{5b}$$

W_c represents channel widths in the Coast basins, and W_a in the Ashnola basins. Both equations are significant at the 1% level (coefficients of determination of .985 and .969 respectively) with standard errors of 13.8 and 12.7%. Data for Slesse Creek were not included because its regional precipitation total falls between regional conditions of the two main areas.

Table I lists the observed and predicted values for the preceding equations. Differences between observed and predicted values may reflect the influence of ponds, log jams, erodibility of sediments, canyons, etc.

Equation 5 illustrates the climatic dependence of the W_D-DA relations. Coast Mountain basins having a larger annual precipitation experience larger possible formative discharges as compared to the drier Ashnola basins. This difference is reflected in the regression constant, which may be interpreted as the channel width for streams with drainage areas of 1 km² (0.4 mi²). Its value is 3.7 m (12 ft) for the coastal basins and 1.3 m (4 ft) for the Ashnola basins.

Similarity of the exponents in Equations 5a and 5b implies a similarity in the channel forming process. Covariance analysis indicates an 85% probability that the slopes of the regression lines are the same. It is thought that these exponents reflect the relative erodibility of the channel lining sediments, which are similar for the two regions (glacial debris). Miller's (1958) work substantiates this to a degree.

145

TABLE II

FLOW DATA

Reach		Discharge Range (m³ s⁻¹)	No. of Runs	a_A 95%			b_A 95%		
				Observed	Confidence Band	Predicted (Eg. 11)	Observed	Confidence Band	Predicted (Eg. 10)
Brockton	1-2	0.00016 — 0.16	10	0.77	0.59 — 0.95	.69	.34	.308 — .370	.29
Brockton	2-3	0.00073 — 0.11	7	0.69	0.62 — 0.76	.66	.28	.270 — .297	.30
Placid	1-2	0.035 — 0.09	4	1.78	0.99 — 2.57	1.45	.34	.219 — .529	.35
Placid	2-3	0.015 — 0.18	5	1.86	1.40 — 2.32	1.55	.31	.243 — .387	.36
Placid	3-4	0.014 — 0.40	6	3.25	3.08 — 3.42	2.98	.48	.433 — .593	.46
Blaney	1-3	0.12 — 1.15	10	3.32	3.15 — 3.49	2.79	.53	.486 — .571	.45
Blaney	3-5	0.092 — 1.17	18	2.96	2.74 — 3.18	2.99	.44	.390 — .494	.46
Blaney	5-4	0.13 — 1.10	9	3.10	2.93 — 3.27	2.84	.54	.459 — .639	.45
Phyllis	1-2	0.31 — 3.48	9	3.05	2.98 — 3.27	2.96	.46	.435 — .482	.45
Phyllis	2-3	0.23 — 3.61	11	2.90	2.81 — 2.99	2.96	.48	.444 — .516	.46
Phyllis	3-4	0.24 — 3.69	9	3.06	2.85 — 3.27	2.93	.40	.343 — .472	.46
Phyllis	4-6	0.24 — 3.72	8	3.06	2.62 — 3.50	3.15	.36	.273 — .464	.46
Phyllis	5	0.36 — 3.41	4	5.51	4.31 — 6.71	3.70	.50	.345 — .729	.48
Furry		0.91 — 13.90	6	2.79	1.85 — 3.73	4.22	.60	.389 — .922	.49
Slesse	1	3.04 — 13.07	4	3.98	2.81 — 5.15	4.30	.52	.358 — .758	.50
Slesse	2	3.23 — 13.94	5	2.79	2.39 — 3.19	3.63	.58	.500 — .655	.52
Slesse	3	4.7 — 22.58	5	3.10	2.48 — 3.75	3.35	.42	.299 — .539	.48
Juniper		0.23 — 2.70	4	3.89	3.24 — 4.54	3.13	.44	.316 — .603	.46
Ewart	1	0.50 — 15.76	5	2.95	2.67 — 3.23	3.78	.59	.506 — .679	.50
Ewart	2	0.45 — 8.08	4	4.42	3.66 — 5.18	4.32	.47	.392 — .552	.55
Ashnola	1	0.79 — 19.03	4	3.78	3.62 — 3.94	3.85	.42	.403 — .440	.51
Ashnola	2	1.50 — 33.85	4						
Ashnola	3	1.58 — 31.52	4						

FLOW PARAMETERS AND AVAILABLE DATA

Coastal Relations

Statistical relations amongst the variables in Equation 4 were established from multiple regressions of the logarithms of DA, W_D, S, a_A and b_A. Data include the reaches of Furry, Phyllis, Blaney, Brockton and the first two of Placid. Placid 3-4 was excluded because of the presence of two artificial pools.

Regression equations showing the statistical relationship between channel dimensions, W_D and S, and the flow equation parameters are

$$b_A = 0.30 \ W_D^{0.16} \tag{6}$$

$$a_A = 0.83 \ W_D^{0.55} \tag{7}$$

The coefficients of variation are 0.63 and 0.97; standard errors are 14.8% and 6.4%. With 11 degrees of freedom both equations are significant at the 1% level. Again slope is not significant at the 5% level. However, adding S to equation 6 (b_A) increases the co-efficient of variation by 10% (0.73), indicating that slope may have some physical effect on the storage-discharge relations. Standard errors, with (13.2% and 6.3%) and without slope, are essentially the same.

Similar regression analysis of DA, S, a_A and b_A give the following relations

$$b_A = 0.37 \ DA^{0.08} \tag{8}$$

$$a_A = 1.66 \ DA^{0.29} \tag{9}$$

DA explains 59.7% and 98.1% of the variation in b_A and a_A respectively. Standard errors are 15.4% and 5.28%. Both equations are significant at the 1% level. (Including slope in the equations gives coefficients of variation of 0.70 and 0.98 and standard errors of 14% and 4.9% respectively.)

General Equations

Since the relation between channel dimensions and flow equation parameters is independent of climate, general equations can be constructed using the data for the Coast, Slesse and Ashnola basins. These are

147

$$b_A = 0.30 \ W_D{}^{0.17} \tag{10}$$

$$a_A = 0.90 \ W_D{}^{0.47} \tag{11}$$

Coefficients of variation are 0.61 and 0.93, standard errors of 13.1% and 8.3%. Significance is again at the 1% level with 19 degrees of freedom. Juniper Creek was not included in these equations because of the extreme effect of log jams.

DISCUSSION

Interpretation

The marginal significance of slope is not surprising as energy dissipation in rough channels occurs mainly through frequent hydraulic jumps rather than by boundary friction. The effect of slope will decrease with increasing channel roughness (steeper slopes) as proportionally more of the flow occurs in pools and jumps. Slope also appears to have little effect on the channel forming process (Equation 5) suggesting that the pool sequence still exists during very high discharges, particularly in the steeper channels.

Channel width alone explains 32% to 34% more of the variance of the a_A's than the b_A's because the former reflects the storage characteristics of the stream (a_A is the flow area at a discharge of one cubic meter per second) and therefore is directly related to channel and pool size. The exponent, on the other hand, appears to be more sensitive to other channel dimensions; slope for example, explaining 10% of the variance.

The constant is better defined for coastal streams than for the total sample with a coefficient of determination of 0.97, as compared to 0.93. This difference results from the sensitivity of the a_A's to pool storage. The three test reaches having more uniform channel profiles (Ashnola 1, Slesse 1 and 3) have lower a_A values (3.18, 2.79 and 2.79 respectively).

Accuracy

Table II lists the observed and predicted (Equations 10 and 11 only) values for a_A and b_A. The 95% confidence band about the observed values has been calculated to test the local accuracy of the predictions. As this test is sensitive to the number of degrees of freedom, it must be applied with caution to the Q-A relations with less than about 6 degrees of freedom (cf number of runs in Table II).

148

The three sets of linear regression equations predict quite accurately the steady flow conditions in rougher, pooled channels, except where extreme or atypical conditions prevail: large pools on Furry; road constriction on Ashnola 3; several large log jams on Phyllis 1-2. In some cases prediction errors are compensating (e.g. Placid 2-3, Ewart 1 and 2).

The most serious errors occur on the more uniform channels, with a_A's being consistently higher and the b_A' being consistently lower (i.e. Slesse 3). This latter feature suggests a different mode of adjustment to discharge between the two channel types, with the rougher (and generally smaller) channels adjusting more through velocity than through flow area. The increase of b_A with increasing channel width has also been noted by Coates (1969).

CONCLUSIONS

The free parameters of the storage-drainage functions for steep, natural channels can be related to readily available channel (width) and basin (drainage area) dimensions by considering the channels as self-forming.

The most interesting result developed here is that the storage-discharge relations can be considered independent of channel slope. However, it must be stressed that the reasoning for this is statistical, not physical; slope does appear to influence the structure of the relations to a very minor degree.

Chapter 4-3
HYDRAULIC GEOMETRY IN THE GREEN AND BIRKENHEAD BASINS, BRITISH COLUMBIA.

John R. Ponton*

Green and Birkenhead Rivers flow into Lillooet River near Pemberton, British Columbia, about 145 km (91 mi) northeast of Vancouver. Both rivers drain areas of late Mesozoic and Cenozoic volcanic, metavolcanic, and metasedimentary rocks (Mathews, personal communication) which appear to have little structural control over the drainage pattern. Pleistocene glaciation has left the most marked imprint upon the character of the drainage within these basins. Drainage divides in some places are poorly defined; hanging valleys, water falls, and deep canyons are abundant. Glaciers still cover approximately 8% of the Green basin and 1% of the Birkenhead. The proportionally greater glacial area in the Green basin is due to its higher available relief (2660 m or 8700 ft as compared with 2170 m or 7100 ft) and high precipitation input. Estimated mean annual precipitation in the Green ranges from 750 mm (30 in) to a high which may exceed 3750 mm (150 in), while the maximum precipitation in the higher reaches of the Birkenhead probably does not exceed 2500 mm (100 in). Mean maximum daily discharges occur in late June and July, a result of snowmelt, but the absolute maximum discharges have occurred during autumn rains. The mean monthly discharge per km^2 for the Birkenhead basin is lower than that of the Green for all months, reflecting the lower input of precipitation.

Hydraulic geometry reflects the mutual adjustment of the dependent parameters of a stream to changing discharge (cf Leopold and Maddock, 1953). During 1970, data to determine downstream hydraulic geometry was collected along Green and Birkenhead Rivers. Because of the relative inaccessibility of most of the area only a small number of sections were surveyed, using a technique similar to that outlined by Leopold and Skibitzke (1967). No at-a-station data were collected; however, by using data collected by the Water Survey of Canada for the five gauging stations in the area, representative at-a-station curves were also

---

*The financial support of the University of British Columbia Research Fund is gratefully acknowledged.

constructed. Sectional measurements made at gauging stations are not the best suited for determining the station's hydraulic geometry, for slightly different sections may be used at different discharges. This will account for an undeterminable portion of the scatter about the derived relationships. Amongst the five stations considered, this type of scatter will probably be greatest for the two stations Green at Green Lake and Birkenhead, where both wading and cableway measurements were made.

SECTIONAL HYDRAULIC GEOMETRY

Mean Relationships

The sectional hydraulic geometry shows the change in the dependent parameters with changing discharge at a section. Width, cross-sectional area, mean depth, and mean velocity were related to the discharge at each of the five gauging stations. No relationship between slope and discharge was determined, but Wolman (1955) has shown that slope changes only slowly with discharge. Logarithmic transforms of the data were made, and least square regression was used to relate the dependent parameters to discharge. The values of the exponents of the derived power equations compare favorably with values found by other workers in various areas (Table I; Figure 1). Width shows a slightly slower rate of increase while mean depth changes in a manner similar to depth changes elsewhere. Mean velocity appears to vary more rapidly than is usual.

The rate of variation of the Darcy-Weisbach flow resistance number, $f\!f$, was computed for each section from the relation $f\!f \propto Q^{f+z-2m}$ (cf Leopold, Wolman, and Miller, 1964). Assuming the rate of change of slope, z, to be near 0, the average value of y is -0.63, where $f\!f \propto Q^y$. This rate of change is approximately twice as great as that found for streams in non-cohesive materials (Leopold, Wolman, and Miller, 1964). Church (1970) found a similar value in sandur channels on Baffin Island; and from the average values of the exponents, resistance decreased slightly more rapidly (-0.69) for sections along Brandy-wine Creek (Wolman, 1955). Church suggested that the rapid decrease in resistance was due to a "live" bed at higher flows, an increase in "straight through" flow which decreased the influence of the pool and riffle sequence, and the damping of turbulence by rapidly increasing sediment discharge.

The bed and bank materials of the Birkenhead and Green sections are typical of those associated with channels with coarse noncohesive boundaries, but it is possible that the larger size of the material tends to cause the channels to respond in a manner

152

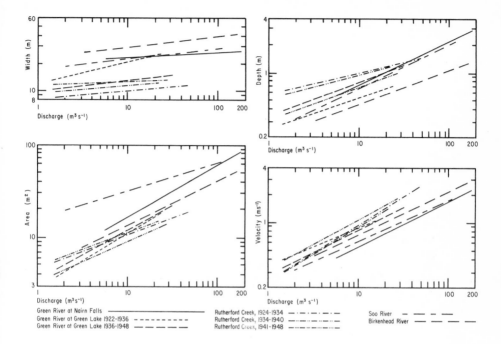

Green River at Nairn Falls ———————— Rutherford Creek, 1924-1934 —·—·—·—·— Soo River — — — —
Green River at Green Lake 1922-1936 —————————— Rutherford Creek, 1934-1940 —··—··—··— Birkenhead River ——— —— —
Green River at Green Lake 1936-1948 — — — — — Rutherford Creek, 1941-1948 —···—···—···—

Figure 1 - At-a-station hydraulic geometry for
eight sections in Birkenhead and
Green Rivers.

typical of channels with cohesive boundaries. Sand size material
is most easily eroded, while smaller material, such as that found
along Brandywine Creek, and larger material are less easily put
into motion by flowing water. It appears that as the sediment size
of the bed and banks increases beyond sand size, the channel
responds in a manner more typical of a channel with cohesive banks.
Soo River, where bed and banks are nearest to sand size, has a
channel response more nearly like other channels in fine noncohesive material while Rutherford Creek, where the largest material
is found, has a rate of change in resistance similar to that of
Brandywine Creek.

The rate of change of velocity also appears to be
associated with other sectional characteristics, with the most
rapid change in velocity associated with the steepest channel,
Rutherford Creek, and the least rapid change associated with the

channel with the least slope, Soo River. Width changes appear to be associated with the local geology of the section: the most rapid increases in width are associated with channels in fluvial deposits.

Residuals

The degree to which the data vary about the mean condition reflected by the hydraulic geometry equations is seen via the coefficients of determination which are derived from the regression analyses and are a measure of the degree to which the equations fit the data. The scatter is consistently greatest about the width relationship (Table I). Langbein (1964), in his theoretical derivation of the hydraulic geometry equations, considered width to be essentially independent at a station in cohesive channels, and not adjustable in a short period of time. Greater variance in the width relations and more distinctive residual groupings support this consideration. Velocity and cross-sectional area have the least scatter for they are largely dependent on discharge and may adjust rapidly over a short period of time.

When the residual values of the regressions were listed as an ordered sequence in time, groupings of positive and negative values appeared (Figure 2). For Green River at Green Lake, two groups of residuals were present with the change occurring in 1936, the year the gauging section was relocated. The residuals of cross-sectional area do not show the grouping as clearly as the residuals of width indicating that area is more dependent on discharge and less dependent on the location of the section. Rutherford Creek shows three similar, though less distinctive, residual groupings. The data for these sections were divided on the basis of the residual groupings and separate hydraulic geometry relations were computed for each grouping. New residual groupings once again appeared, but the new pattern was similar to the pattern observed at the other three sections (cf Figure 2b for Birkenhead data).

A pattern of a number of positive residuals followed by a number of negative ones existed in all relations, though it was not distinctive throughout. This would suggest that the data do not fluctuate about the regression line in a totally random way. Rather, the section appears to fluctuate slowly about the mean condition expressed by the regression line, a type of behavior which Langbein and Leopold (1964) have suggested is typical of a channel which has reached "quasi-equilibrium."

The at-a-station hydraulic geometries for ten other sections on streams in the Coast Mountains were also investigated and were found to be similar to Green and Birkenhead sections

TABLE I

AT-A-STATION HYDRAULIC GEOMETRY[1]

Streams	b	R^2	f	R^2	m	R^2	l	R^2	y
Green at Nairn Falls	0.06	0.39	0.47	0.87	0.46	0.86	0.53	0.89	-0.46
Green at Green Lake,									
1922-1936	0.22	0.38	0.36	0.60	0.42	0.82	0.57	0.91	-0.48
1936-1948	0.14	0.52	0.37	0.71	0.49	0.78	0.52	0.79	-0.60
Soo	0.11	0.53	0.47	0.88	0.42	0.91	0.48	0.93	-0.37
Birkenhead	0.12	0.54	0.36	0.86	0.48	0.81	0.48	0.93	-0.59
Rutherford, 1924-1934	0.12	0.63	0.26	0.83	0.62	0.98	0.38	0.95	-0.98
1934-1940	0.11	0.74	0.29	0.76	0.60	0.94	0.40	0.87	-0.91
1941-1948	0.06	0.30	0.40	0.92	0.54	0.93	0.46	0.91	-0.68
Coast Mountain Streams in British Columbia, mean[2]	0.21		0.32		0.50		0.49		-0.73
Baffin Island sandurs, mean[3]	0.22		0.31		0.48		0.52		-0.65
Midwestern U.S., mean[4]	0.26		0.40		0.34				
Brandywine Creek, Pennsylvania[5]	0.04		0.41		0.55				
Average of 158 U.S. streams[6]	0.12		0.45		0.43				

[1] width=aQ^b; depth=cQ^f; velocity=kQ^m; sectional area=jQ^l; ff $\propto Q^y$
[2] Ponton, thesis in progress
[3] Church, 1970
[4] Leopold and Maddock, 1953
[5] Wolman, 1955
[6] Leopold, Wolman and Miller, 1964

155

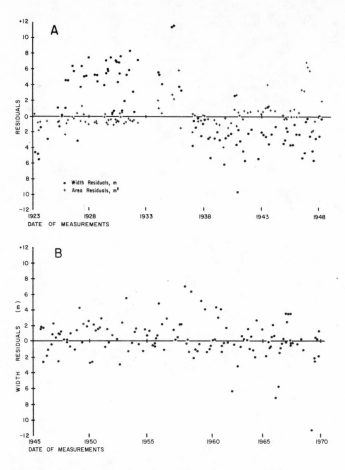

Figure 2 - Residuals of sectional area width:
    (a) Green River at Green Lake
    (b) Birkenhead River (width only)

(Table I).   The adjustment of the hydraulic
parameters in this region appears to be different from that of some
other regions, with lower rates of width adjustment, a dominant
velocity adjustment, and a rapid change in resistance.

DOWNSTREAM HYDRAULIC GEOMETRY

The downstream hydraulic geometry shows a greater
departure from other results reported in the literature.   These
values must be viewed with more caution than the at-a-station
results for only a small amount of data was collected.   Ten sections
were measured within the Birkenhead basin and six within the

Green. The form of analysis was similar to that for at-a-station data. The discharge at each section was found from the relation between drainage area and $Q_{2.33}$ (mean annual flood) for the five gauging stations. These hydraulic geometry relations show the change in the dependent hydraulic parameters as the magnitude of a flow of constant frequency increases downstream.

Width shows the most rapid increase within the channel system, while mean depth increases less rapidly (Table II, Figure 3). Mean velocity tends to decrease slowly, while slope decreases rapidly. The Darcy-Weisbach resistance factor also decreases rapidly. The increase in width is more rapid than in other areas

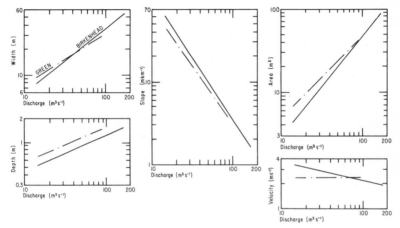

Figure 3 - Downstream hydraulic geometry
for Birkenhead and Green Rivers.

that have been studied, and depth increases slightly more rapidly (Table II). Channels in this area appear to have a more rapidly increasing width to depth ratio than those in other areas, indicating that the headwater channels are relatively narrow and deep while downstream reaches are relatively wide and shallow. In their upstream reaches, channels in this area are controlled by large bed and bank materials while downstream reaches are less confined because of smaller material which can be moved more often by the streams.

Velocity shows the greatest departure from previous studies. For each basin, velocity shows a decrease in the down-stream direction. The average value of the velocity exponent is -0.11; all other workers have found that the average change in velocity is positive. The large scatter of the data about the velocity-discharge relations suggests that they may be suspect. One possible cause of this large scatter is the estimation of the $Q_{2.33}$ velocity at each section.

TABLE II

DOWNSTREAM HYDRAULIC GEOMETRY[1]

Streams	b	R^2	f	R^2	m	R^2	l	R^2	z	R^2	y'
Green River	.60	.70	.40	.42	-.01	.00	1.00	.63	-1.29	.32	-0.89
Birkenhead River	.80	.94	.44	.94	-.23	.48	1.17	.89	-1.54	.37	-0.64
Brandywine Creek, Pennsylvania[2]	.42		.45		.05				-1.07		
Midwestern U.S., mean[3]	.5		.4		.1				-0.49		
Ephemeral streams, U.S.[4]	.5		.3		.2				-0.95		
Appalachian streams[5]	.55		.36		.09						
High mountain streams[6]	.38		.25		.39						

[1] width=aQ^b; depth=cQ^f; velocity=kQ^m; sectional area=jQ^l; slope=tQ^z; ff QY'
[2] Wolman, 1955
[3] Leopold and Maddock, 1953
[4] Leopold and Miller, 1956
[5] Brush, 1961
[6] Miller, 1958

158

Another possibility is that there is no or only a slight systematic change in velocity with increasing downstream discharge. The coefficient of determination, R^2, is 0.00 for Green River data implying no simple relation. The R^2 for Birkenhead, 0.48, is low and implies only a slight power function relationship. (Similarly low values were found when regressions were run on one set of data collected by Miller (1958) on Pecos River ($R^2 = 0.01$) and three sets of data collected by Brush (1961) on Little Juniata (0.30), Standing Stone (0.22), and Shaver (0.55).)

The decrease in velocity may, however, be a real result of the rapid change in channel slope. Though Langbein and Leopold (1964) have suggested that the theoretical maximum decrease in slope would be proportional to Q^{-1}, the average value of the exponent for this area is -1.40. Slopes still appear to be strongly controlled by the effects of glaciation and may be independent of discharge. This is almost surely the case in the headwater reaches as Day (1970) pointed out in his study of high mountain streams in southwestern British Columbia. Slopes in the lower reaches are probably partly a result of stream activity, but they can not be assumed to be completely dependent on discharge. Hence, the rapidly decreasing slope must be at least partially independent of channel conditions.

Leopold (1953) suggested that an observed increase in velocity downstream was due to the increase in depth and the decrease in resistance. These changes were sufficiently great to compensate for the decrease in slope, which would tend to decrease velocity. In Green and Birkenhead basins the decrease in slope would appear to be greater than decreasing resistance and increasing depth can compensate, resulting in a decrease in velocity downstream.

CONCLUSION

The departure of the downstream hydraulic geometry of Green and Birkenhead Rivers from previous works may be an effect of the recent glaciation in the area and the strong control which glacial features have on the streams. It would appear that equilibrium throughout the entire channel system of both streams has not yet been established. Many reaches within each system may have arrived at a quasi-equilibrium, as the at-a-station hydraulic geometry seems to indicate. However, these reaches are not yet adjusted to each other because of glacial features which separate them and in part control their development. Other factors, such as the rapid decrease in slope and its partial independence would suggest that a graded state has not been reached. Reports

have been made of rapid degradation along some sections, evidence
of aggradation and degradation exists along certain reaches, and
waterfalls are found on all of the main rivers and many of the
tributaries. The different manner of downstream channel adjustment found in these two systems would appear to be the result of
non-equilibrium conditions.

Chapter 4-4

SEDIMENT CHANGES ON TWO ALLUVIAL FANS
IN THE CANADIAN ROCKY MOUNTAINS.

H. J. McPherson and F. Hirst*

A distinctive landform occurring in the Canadian Rocky Mountains is the alluvial fan. Although many researchers have investigated the morphology, sedimentary characteristics and formation of alluvial fans in semi-desert regions (see for example, Blackwelder, 1928; Sharpe, 1938: Blissenbach, 1954; Beaty, 1963; Bull, 1964; Bluck, 1964; Denny and Drewes, 1965; Beaty, 1970), only a few have studied alluvial fans in cold temperate high mountain areas (Hoppe and Eckman, 1964; Winder, 1965; Broscoe and Thompson, 1969).

In the Kootenay plains area of the upper North Saskatchewan valley in the Canadian Rockies a series of well developed, often coalescing alluvial fans exist. This paper describes the variations in sediment character which occur over the surface of two of these fans and shows how these changes are related to fan surface slope, distance from the fan apex and lithology.

DESCRIPTION

Two O'clock and Bridge Creeks are left bank tributaries of the upper North Saskatchewan river in west central Alberta (Figure 1). Following the retreat of the last Wisconsin glacier the two streams built coalescing alluvial fans on the broad floor of the North Saskatchewan valley (McPherson, 1971).

Although both fans have surface areas of 0.75 mi^2 (1.9 km^2) the drainage area of Bridge Creek is larger, $(6.1 \text{ mi}^2;$ $4.6 \text{ km}^2)$ than that of Two O'clock Creek, $(3.5 \text{ mi}^2; 2.6 \text{ km}^2)$.

The apex of Two O'clock Creek fan lies at an elevation of 4927 ft (1502 m) while the relative relief between apex and toe

*The financial support of the National Research Council of Canada is gratefully acknowledged.

is 575 ft (175 m). Bridge Creek fan apex lies at an elevation of 4712 ft (1437 m) and the relative relief is 395 ft (120 m). Longitudinal profiles for the fans reveal that they possess smooth concave upwards profiles with surface slope values increasing towards the apexes (Figure 2).

The upper one-fifth of Two O'clock and Bridge Creek drainage basins lie within the Main Ranges subprovince of the Canadian Rockies while the lower four-fifths are in the Front Ranges subprovince. The Borgeau thrust fault (Figure 3) is the boundary between the two subprovinces and crosses the watershed at an elevation of approximately 7000 ft (2134 m). Bedrock outcropping in the basins ranges in age from Mississippian to Proterozoic and includes the Stephen, Cathedral, Rundle, Rocky Mountain and Fernice formations and the Gog, Miette, and Spray River groups. The fans are underlain by the Sulphur Mountain and Rundle formations (Figure 3). The former consists of shales and silty dolomites while the latter is made up of crinoidal limestones and dolomites which outcrop at several locations.

During the summers of 1969 and 1970 a gauging station was maintained several hundred feet upstream from the apex of Two O'clock fan. For most of the period the mean daily discharge was less than 10 cusecs (0.28 m^3s^{-1}) with a maximum mean daily discharge of 43 cusecs (1.2 m^3s^{-1}) in 1969 and 42 cusecs (1.18 m^3s^{-1}) in 1970.

Precipitation in the Kootenay plains region is well below the average for the eastern slopes of the Rockies. The average annual precipitation is 11.1 in (28.2 cm) with the highest and lowest recorded values being 16.6 in (2.1 cm) and 5.6 in (13.2 cm) respectively.

The upper segments of the basins, above approximately 7000 ft (2134 m) are bare or carry a scanty cover of alpine tundra vegetation. Below treeline the basin slopes are vegetated with a moderately dense cover of Lodgepole Pine and Engelmann Spruce while the fan surfaces have a cover typified by extensive natural open grassy meadows and small stands of deciduous aspen and balsam poplar.

AGE AND FAN MORPHOLOGY

Following the melting of the last Wisconsin glacier from the North Saskatchewan valley a lateral moraine and three terraces were left in the section of the valley where Two O'clock and Bridge Creeks join the North Saskatchewan (Figure 1). The highest terrace stands approximately 40 ft (12.2 m) above present river

162

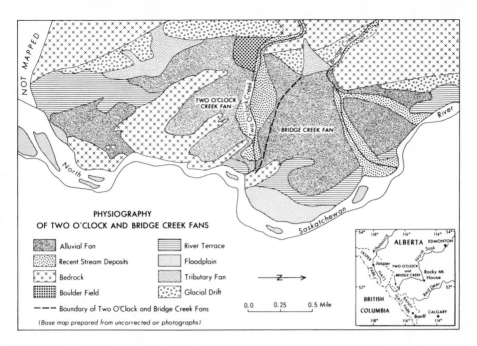

PHYSIOGRAPHY
OF TWO O'CLOCK AND BRIDGE CREEK FANS

- Alluvial Fan
- Recent Stream Deposits
- Bedrock
- Boulder Field
- River Terrace
- Floodplain
- Tributary Fan
- Glacial Drift

- - - Boundary of Two O'Clock and Bridge Creek Fans

(Base map prepared from uncorrected air photographs)

0.0   0.25   0.5 Mile

4-4   Figure 1 - Physiography of Two O'Clock and
Bridge Creek Fans

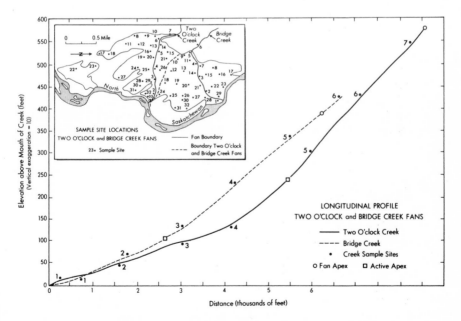

SAMPLE SITE LOCATIONS
TWO O'CLOCK and BRIDGE CREEK FANS
—— Fan Boundary
- - - Boundary Two O'clock
       and Bridge Creek Fans
23• Sample Site

LONGITUDINAL PROFILE
TWO O'CLOCK and BRIDGE CREEK FANS
—— Two O'clock Creek
- - - Bridge Creek
• Creek Sample Sites
○ Fan Apex   ☐ Active Apex

Elevation above Mouth of Creek (feet)
(Vertical exaggeration = 10)

Distance (thousands of feet)

Figure 2 - Longitudinal profiles: Two O'Clock
and Bridge Creek Fans

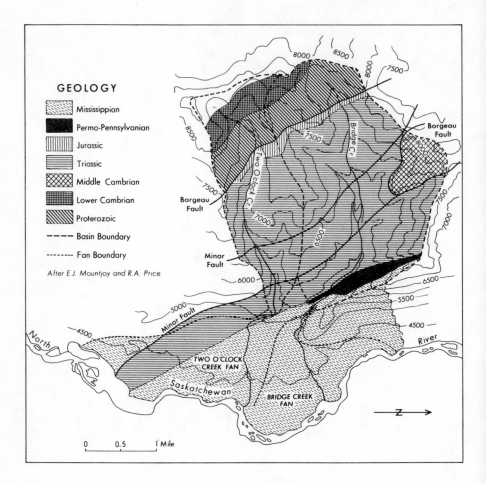

Figure 3 - Geology of study area

level. Two O'clock and Bridge Creek fans have been built over the two lower terraces and around a series of cherty limestone ridges which are present on the valley floor (Figure 1).

Incorporated in the near surface deposits and extending over much of the fan surface area is a layer of volcanic ash. This material has been identified as Bridge River ash and was laid down between 2120 ± 150 and 2670 ± 140 years before present (Westgate and Dreimanis, 1967). The existence of the terraces underneath the fan deposits and the presence of the volcanic ash in the fan sediments establishes that most fan accumulation occurred in the post-glacial period prior to approximately 2000 B.P.

Surface slope values vary over the fans from a high of 6.5° close to the apexes to 0.5° near the toes. In general the fan surfaces are relatively smooth and no distinct elevation breaks occur.

The lower parts of the channels of Two O'clock and Bridge Creeks are on a level with or slightly higher than the adjacent fan surfaces while above the active apexes (Figure 2), the streams are incised below the fan surfaces. During above average flow periods the creeks spill out of their poorly defined channels below the active apexes and fresh sediment is deposited over the lower sections of the fans.

In the apex zone of Two O'clock Creek a boulder field occurs (Figure 1). This consists of a number of very large sub-rounded boulders separated by a series of channels which are infilled with cobbles. The largest boulder measured was 18 ft long (5.5 m); 10 ft wide (3 m) and 6 ft high (1.8 m) while the cobbles averaged approximately 1 ft (0.3 m) in diameter. The boulder field materials are believed to be mud flow deposits which have been reworked by wash action resulting in the winnowing out of the fine grained size fraction.

SAMPLING

Sediments were analyzed at 26 sites on Two O'clock Creek fan surface and at 26 sites on Bridge Creek fan surface. Sample sites were spaced at 990 ft (302 m) intervals and sample locations were determined by superimposing a 990 ft grid (302 m) on an aerial photograph mosaic of the fans so that the sample lines ran north-south. After the first site was located the pace and compass method was used to find subsequent positions. Locations for the sample sites are given in Figure 2.

A typical stratigraphic section at a sample site on the

165

fan surfaces consisted of a variable thickness of silt and clay overlying gravel and sand. As the silt and clay layer was a vertical accretion deposit only the underlying gravel was sampled.

The sampling procedure at each location was as follows. A pit was dug through the vertical accretion sediments and triaxial tests and lithology determinations were made on the first 50 pebbles with larger than 0.5 in (1.27 cm) median diameters. A volumetric sample of between 10 lbs (4.5 kg) and 15 lbs (6.7 kg) was collected for later mechanical analysis using the combined sieve/pipette method.

In addition 7 samples from Two O'clock Creek and 6 samples from Bridge Creek were taken from the creek beds.

As the sediments in the creek beds were not veneered with silt and clay a different sampling procedure was employed. A 20 ft (6.1 m) length of cord knotted at 1 ft (0.3 m) intervals was placed sequentially in the four cardinal directions and the pebble lying directly beneath each knot was selected. The lithology of the pebble and the lengths of its three axes were recorded together with the radius of curvature of the smallest convex segment of the pebble circumference (r value) measured in the principal plane of the pebble. If rotation through the four cardinal directions failed to give the required 50 pebbles because the knot fell on material smaller than 0.5 in (1.27 cm) the cord was rotated in the inter-mediate directions.

ANALYSES

Values for the means of the major, intermediate and minor axes, volume, maximum projection area, roundness and flatness were computed for the gravels at each site together with their standard deviations. The sedimentary parameters were determined from the following formulae:

Volume = (π /6). LM S (Sneed and Folk, 1958).
Maximum Projection Area =
$\qquad$ (3 $\sqrt{\text{LMS}}$)^2 . π /4 (Sneed and Folk, 1958).
Roundness = 2 r . 1000/L (Cailleux; 1963).
Flatness = (L + M)/ 2 . S (Cailleux, 1963).

where L is the length of the major pebble axis, M is the length of the intermediate pebble axis, S is length of the minor pebble axis and r is the radius of curvature of the smallest convex segment of the pebble's circumference measured in the principal plane of the pebble.

The various indices calculated express the size, form and hydraulic behaviour of the pebbles. Maximum projection area refers to the cross-sectional area of the pebble which is exposed to settling in water and is a measure of the drag exerted on the particle in settling while the roundness and flatness indices are expressions of pebble shape (McPherson, 1961). Standard deviation values for the mean axial lengths express the size dispersion of the sample and are therefore sorting coefficients. A large standard deviation value indicates a very poorly sorted deposit.

RESULTS

To determine how sediment characteristics vary over the fan surfaces the means for the three axes, volume, maximum projection area, roundness and flatness were correlated using the least squares method with distance (in 10^3 ft) from the fan apex and with local fan surface slope (in °). As the distributions at each site were skewed the dependent variables in each case were log normalized. Standard deviation values for each of the sedimentary parameters were also correlated with distance and local slope to discover how sample dispersion changed over the fan surfaces. In the regression equations (Tables I and II) axial size is expressed in ins, maximum projection area in ins^2; volume in ins^3 while the roundness and flatness values are dimensionless.

The sedimentary characteristics of the pebbles in the stream beds were correlated against channel slope and distance from the fan apex to permit comparisons to be made with the relationships established for the fan surfaces.

Fan Surface Samples

Significant relationships were found to exist between axial size, volume, maximum projection area, roundness and distance from the fan apex. Size, volume and maximum projection area decrease downfan while roundness values increase. This result is confirmed by reference to Figures 4 and 5. Fan surface slope correlated significantly with axial size, volume, maximum projection area and roundness. The smaller better rounded pebbles with lower maximum projection area values are associated with the gentler slopes (Table I).

Roundness values for Two O'clock Creek fan varied from 94 to 256 and for Bridge Creek fan between 95 and 249. These values show that the gravels are at best poorly rounded. Flatness values for Two O'clock fan ranged from 1.64 to 2.68 and between 1.64 to 2.33 for Bridge Creek fan indicating that the gravels closely approach an equidimensional cross-section.

167

TABLE I

Simple Regression of Slope Against Sedimentary Parameters for Fan Surface for Two O'Clock Creek Fan

Dependent Variable (Y)	Equation	R	Significance* Level
Mean L	Y = 0.1622 + 0.0499 X	0.8647	At 1% Level
Standard Deviation L	Y = - 0.3088 + 0.0843 X	0.7438	At 1% Level
Mean M	Y = 0.0254 + 0.0489 X	0.8565	At 1% Level
Standard Deviation M	Y = - 0.4537 + 0.0818 X	0.7286	At 1% Level
Mean S	Y = - 0.1557 + 0.0477 X	0.8178	At 1% Level
Standard Deviation S	Y = - 0.5577 + 0.0805 X	0.7583	At 1% Level
Mean Volume	Y = - 0.1001 + 0.1759 X	0.7974	At 1% Level
Standard Deviation Volume	Y = 0.0586 + 0.1631 X	0.6406	At 1% Level
Mean Maximum Projection Area	Y = 0.1276 + 0.1097 X	0.8376	At 1% Level
Standard Deviation Maximum Projection Area	Y = 0.0093 + 0.1388 X	0.7236	At 1% Level
Mean Roundness	Y = 2.3304 - 0.0427 X	- 0.8344	At 1% Level
Standard Deviation Roundness	Y = 1.9562 - 0.0281 X	- 0.4982	At 2% Level
Mean Flatness, Standard Deviation Flatness			Not Significant

Simple Regression of Slope Against Sedimentary Parameters for Fan Surface for Bridge Creek Fan

Dependent Variable (Y)	Equation	R	Significance* Level
Mean L	Y = 0.1085 + 0.0620 X	0.7229	At 1% Level
Standard Deviation L	Y = - 0.4732 + 0.1264 X	0.6893	At 1% Level
Mean M	Y = - 0.0310 + 0.0583 X	0.7097	At 1% Level
Standard Deviation M	Y = - 0.6750 + 0.1351 X	0.7379	At 1% Level
Mean S	Y = - 0.1961 + 0.0583 X	0.7052	At 1% Level
Standard Deviation S	Y = - 0.7829 + 0.1368 X	0.7678	At 1% Level
Mean Volume	Y = - 0.3641 + 0.2430 X	0.7177	At 1% Level
Standard Deviation Volume	Y = - 0.5590 + 0.3543 X	0.7394	At 1% Level
Mean Maximum Projection Area	Y = - 0.0186 + 0.1416 X	0.7200	At 1% Level
Standard Deviation Maximum Projection Area	Y = - 0.3628 + 0.2555 X	0.5721	At 1% Level
Mean Roundness	Y = 2.3223 - 0.0407 X	- 0.7205	At 1% Level
Mean Flatness, Standard Deviation Flatness, Standard Deviation Roundness			Not Significant

* Relationship not significant below 5% Level.

NOTE: L = Long Axis, M = Intermediate Axis, S = Short Axis, R = Correlation Coefficient.

NOTE: Only Positive Standard Deviations are accepted.

TABLE II

Simple Regression of Slope Against Sedimentary Parameters for Creek Samples for Two O'Clock Creek Fan

Dependent Variable (Y)	Equation	R	Significance Level
Mean L	Y = 0.3411 + 0.0606 X	0.8226	At 2% Level
Standard Deviation L	Y = 0.0226 + 0.1081 X	0.8982	At 1% Level
Mean M	Y = 0.1988 + 0.0557 X	0.8186	At 2% Level
Standard Deviation M	Y = - 0.1390 + 0.1031 X	0.8889	At 1% Level
Mean S	Y = 0.0249 + 0.0533 X	0.7783	At 5% Level
Standard Deviation S	Y = -0.2214 + 0.0919 X	0.8689	At 1% Level
Mean Volume	Y = 0.4977 + 0.2490 X	0.8749	At 1% Level
Standard Deviation Volume	Y = 0.7116 + 0.3055 X	0.8887	At 1% Level
Mean Maximum Projection Area	Y = 0.4934 + 0.1488 X	0.8609	At 1% Level
Standard Deviation Maximum Projection Area	Y = 0.4863 + 0.2067 X	0.9052	At 1% Level
Standard Deviation Roundness	Y = 1.8341 + 0.0306 X	0.7562	At 5% Level
Mean Flatness, Standard Deviation Flatness, Mean Roundness			Not Significant

Simple Regression of Slope Against Sedimentary Parameters for Creek Samples for Bridge Creek Fan

Dependent Variable (Y)	Equation	R	Significance* Level
Mean L	Y = - 0.3339 + 0.2146 X	0.9503	At 1% Level
Standard Deviation L	Y = - 1.0035 + 0.3524 X	0.9310	At 1% Level
Mean M	Y = - 0.4586 + 0.2118 X	0.9550	At 1% Level
Standard Deviation M	Y = - 1.0067 + 0.3217 X	0.9168	At 1% Level
Mean S	Y = - 0.5099 + 0.1756 X	0.9387	At 1% Level
Standard Deviation S	Y = - 0.9923 + 0.2687 X	0.9247	At 1% Level
Mean Volume	Y = - 1.6393 + 0.7481 X	0.9266	At 1% Level
Standard Deviation Volume	Y = - 1.3502 + 0.7769 X	0.8867	At 1% Level
Mean Maximum Projection Area	Y = - 1.0115 + 0.5074 X	0.9440	At 1% Level
Standard Deviation Maximum Projection Area	Y = - 1.1620 + 0.6006 X	0.9050	At 1% Level
Mean Flatness	Y = 0.1663 + 0.0337 X	0.8615	At 1% Level
Mean Roundness	Y = 2.4086 - 0.0688 X	- 0.8756	At 1% Level
Standard Deviation Flatness, Standard Deviation Roundness			Not Significant

*Relationship not significant below 5% Level.

NOTE: L = Long Axis, M = Intermediate Axis,
S = Short Axis.

NOTE: Only Positive Standard Deviation Values are accepted.

The decrease in maximum projection area values downfan demonstrates there is a systematic decrease in the area of resistance to the settling velocities of the particles with increasing distance from the fan apex and with decreasing slope.

Sediment sorting on both fans is significantly related to distance from the apex and to local slope. Sorting increases downfan with the better sorted sediments occurring on the gentler slopes.

To illustrate how pebble characteristics varied over the fan surfaces, values for the mean of the intermediate axis, the standard deviation of the intermediate axis (a sorting measure) volume, maximum projection area and roundness were mapped using the Synagraphic Mapping System (SYMAP) which gives a mechanical plot of the data. The results are given in Figures 4 and 5.

On Two O'clock fan intermediate axial size, volume, maximum projection area and sorting decrease very rapidly in the first 2000 ft (600 m) downfan from the apex (Figure 4). This is associated with a similar rapid decrease in local fan slope. Roundness, however, alters much more slowly downfan.

The pattern of change on Bridge Creek fan is similar (Figure 5). Rapid variations in intermediate axial size, volume and maximum projection area occurs in the first 2000 ft (600 m) while roundness alters in a much less systematic manner.

Comparison of Fan Surface and Creek Bed Samples

Comparisons between the regression equations relating the sedimentary parameters to local fan surface slope for the samples collected from the fan surfaces and those derived for the samples collected from the creek beds (Table II) show a similar systematic variation in sediment character.

Results of the mechanical analyses of fan surface and creek bed materials are presented as cumulative curve bands in Figure 6. For both fans the size distribution range is greater for the fan surface sediments than for the stream bed materials and the stream bed sediments contain lower percentages of the fine grained size fractions. This is partly a consequence of the stream carrying away the finer sized material in suspension, partly the washing down of accretion silts and clays which overlie the gravels and partly the chemical and mechanical breakdown of the sediments in situ.

TABLE III

Two O'Clock Creek Fan: Multiple Correlation of Slope, Distance, Percents Carbonates, Sandstone, Quartzite and Other Lithologies Against Sedimentary Characteristics

Dependent Variable X_1	X_2	X_3	X_4	X_5	X_6	X_7	Multiple Correlation Coefficient	Significance
Mean M	0.85109	-0.6664	-0.37940	0.04787	0.29508	0.64488	0.80931	At 1% Level
Mean Volume	0.59665	-0.49705	-0.29273	-0.16729	0.30693	0.65658	0.70500	At 5% Level
Mean Maximum Projection	0.72608	-0.58529	-0.32711	-0.14692	0.31876	0.68465	0.76275	At 1% Level
Mean Roundness	-0.78478	0.79507	0.54465	-0.12477	-0.38567	-0.52831	0.77925	At 1% Level
Mean Flatness	*Not Significant							

$$X_1 = 2.37566 + 0.16685\ X_2 - 0.00002\ X_3 - 0.00736\ X_4 - 0.01781\ X_5 - 0.02156\ X_6 + 0.00728\ X_7$$

$$X_1 = 57.95733 + 1.53760\ X_2 - 0.00083\ X_3 + 0.68805\ X_4 + 0.44822\ X_5 + 0.46505\ X_6 + 1.72641\ X_7$$

$$X_1 = 16.48854 + 0.76544\ X_2 - 0.00024\ X_3 - 0.09973\ X_4 - 0.22120\ X_5 - 0.21907\ X_6 + 0.14786\ X_7$$

$$X_1 = 815.06250 - 7.55394\ X_2 + 0.00917\ X_3 - 6.85323\ X_4 - 6.39605\ X_5 - 6.30839\ X_6 - 7.54824\ X_7$$

*Not Significant

Dependent Variable X_1	X_2	X_3	X_4	X_5	X_6	X_7	Multiple Correlation Coefficient	Significance
Mean M	0.70177	-0.75901	-0.04472	-0.35251	0.30182	0.02688	0.77021	At 5% Level
Mean Volume	0.51455	-0.62883	-0.23433	-0.28803	0.45948	-0.02036	0.81048	At 1% Level
Mean Maximum Projection Area	0.65076	-0.75241	-0.13422	-0.32976	0.38362	-0.00723	0.82570	At 1% Level
Mean Roundness	-0.70996	0.72820	0.28893	0.04570	-0.33874	0.02249	0.86315	At 1% Level
Mean Flatness	*Not Significant							

$$X_1 = 5.38850 + 0.02516\ X_2 - 0.00021\ X_3 - 0.04350\ X_4 - 0.02343\ X_5 - 0.02043\ X_6 - 0.01243\ X_7$$

$$X_1 = 101.32849 - 1.24934\ X_2 - 0.00474\ X_3 - 1.04810\ X_4 - 0.59917\ X_5 - 0.40481\ X_6 + 0.11583\ X_7$$

$$X_1 = -1.79568 - 0.19947\ X_2 - 0.00165\ X_3 + 0.04096\ X_4 + 0.15661\ X_5 + 0.20391\ X_6 + 0.35896\ X_7$$

$$X_1 = 181.08594 - 7.21584\ X_2 + 0.01170\ X_3 + 0.31450\ X_4 - 1.14154\ X_5 - 1.14029\ X_6 + 0.54103\ X_7$$

*Not Significant

*NOTE: Equations not significant below 5% level.

NOTE: M = Intermediate Axis.

X_2 = Slope X_3 = Distance from Fan Apex X_5 = % Sandstone

X_3 = % Carbonates X_5 = % Sandstone

X_6 = % Quartzite X_7 = % Other Lithology

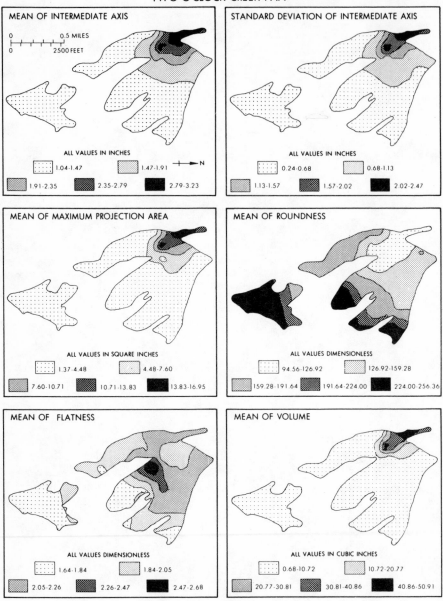

Figure 4 - Two O'Clock Creek Fan: sediment
parameters

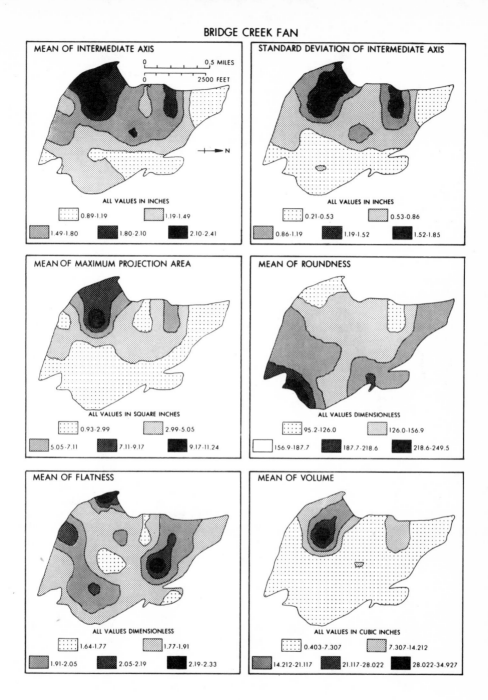

Figure 5 - Bridge Creek Fan: sediment
parameters

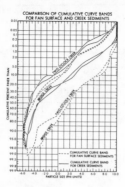

Figure 6 - Comparison of cumulative curve
bands for fan surface and creek
sediment.

Influence of Lithology on Fan Surface Sedimentary Patterns

To evaluate the influence of lithology on the relationships
established between particle size, pebble shape and local fan
surface slope and distance from the fan apex, multiple regression
equations were derived and tested for significance using the F
test. Fan surface slope, distance from the apex, percentage
of carbonate rock, percentage of quartzite, and percentage of
sandstone as the independent variables are related to mean values
for the intermediate axis, volume, maximum projection area,
roundness and flatness. The results are presented in Table III.
With the single exception of flatness all the equations were
found to be significant. Slope was the variable providing the
greatest explanation for Two O'clock Creek fan with distance
from the fan apex second and lithology giving the least explanation.
For Bridge Creek fan distance from the apex provided a slightly
better degree of explanation than local fan surface slope with
lithology accounting for the least explanation of the variance.

DISCUSSION AND CONCLUSIONS

Systematic variations in sediment character over the
surfaces of the fans and the similarity between the patterns of
change for the fan surface sediments and the stream channel
deposits suggests that these two Rocky Mountain alluvial fans
were formed primarily as a result of stream deposition.

The importance of mudflows in alluvial fan development
has been stressed by many researchers, especially those working
in the semi-arid and arid environments of the southwestern United
States (see for example; Sharpe, 1938; Croft, 1962; Lustig, 1965;
Beaty, 1970). Winder (1965) proposed that an alluvial fan in the

174

upper Smokey region of Alberta, approximately 130 mi (208 km) north of Two O'clock Creek was the result of mudflow deposition and suggested that mudflow action might well be the dominant process contributing to alluvial fan formation in alpine regions. The results of this study suggest the dominance of fluvial action in the formation of Two O'clock and Bridge Creek fans. The presence of a small boulder field in the apex zone of Two O'clock Creek fan suggests that mudflows may have contributed to fan development, but only to a minor degree. Further fieldwork on several other fans in the same area indicates the primary role played by fluvial action in fan formation. This suggests that possibly stream deposition rather than mudflow action may be the more important process in constructing high mountain alluvial fans in cold temperate regions.

Particle size decreases rapidly downfan from the apex while sediment sorting increases. Both changes are associated with a sharp reduction in fan surface slope. These changes in sediment size, local fan slope and sorting illustrate the rapidity with which selective transport adjustment takes place between the variables of pebble size, local slope and distance when a stream changes from being a primarily transporting medium, as Two O'clock and Bridge Creeks are above their apexes, to an aggrading depositional system. Pebble rounding increases significantly downfan but much less dramatically than either size or sorting and the particles even at the fan toes are poorly rounded.

Results of the linear and multiple regression analyses relating sediment characteristics to local fan slope, distance from the apex and lithology indicate that slope and distance provide the greatest explanation of the variance for sediment change and lithology the least. McPherson (1971) studied changes in sediment character from the source to mouth of Two O'clock Creek and found that lithology was the single most important factor controlling particle size, shape and sorting. The findings of this research indicate that when a stream is aggrading that lithology becomes much less important than either local slope or distance from the apex in determining the pattern of sediment deposition. However, when the stream is primarily concerned with transportation and is being constantly supplied with fresh material along its course lithology is the overriding factor determining sediment character (McPherson, 1971).

175

Chapter 4-5

AGGRADATION AND CHANNEL PATTERNS
OF THE ALEXANDRA-NORTH SASKATCHEWAN RIVER,
BANFF NATIONAL PARK, ALBERTA.

D. G. Smith*

The Alexandra-North Saskatchewan River system is
located southeast of the Columbia Icefield in the northwest part of
Banff National Park, Alberta. The area studied consists of a
stretch of river bottom-land, 13 km (8 mi) long by nearly 1 km
(1/2 mi) wide, of the Alexandra and North Saskatchewan rivers
(Figure 1).

The principle objective of this study is to examine an
aggrading river and to determine its processes, rates of deposition,
and causes of variations in channel pattern. The North Saskatchewan
River is one of many glacier-fed rivers in the Canadian Cordillera

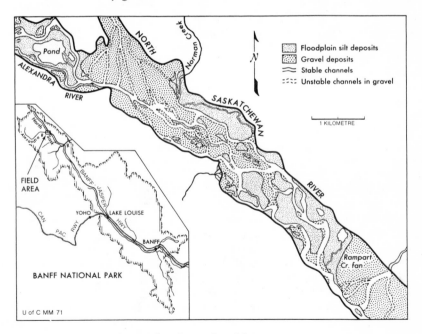

Figure 1 - Location Map

*The financial support of the Johns Hopkins University,
the Geological Society of America and the Inland Waters Branch,
Canada Department of Energy, Mines and Resources is gratefully
acknowledged.
177

displaying bottom-land features characteristic of aggrading rivers. Such features include a combination of braided channels, absence of terraces, large volumes of sediment transport, and rapid decrease in channel gradient downstream.

REGIONAL SETTING

The North Saskatchewan River flows southeast through a steep-sided, glacially deepened valley. The relief between the valley floor and high, ice-covered mountain peaks varies between 1200 and 1800 m (4000 and 6000 ft). Width of the valley floor varies between 600 and 900 m (2000 and 3000 ft); materials on the floor consist entirely of fluvial sediments. Adjacent hillslopes are mantled with deposits of till, which thin upslope to timberline at an elevation of 2100 m (7000 ft), (McPherson, 1970). Both the local bedrock and river gravel consist of meta-sedimentary rocks, largely limestone, dolomite, shale and quartzite.

The river bottom-land consists of three reaches of alluvial silts separated by two gravel reaches which are being deposited by the North Saskatchewan River and Rampart Creek (Figure 1). The gravel deposits extend across the valley floor to form alluvial fans, thus contracting the channels of both the Alexandra and lower North Saskatchewan Rivers. These deposits will here be termed primary alluvial fans because their presence directly affects the entire river-bottom morphology. Downriver from each contraction, secondary alluvial fans have developed. These fan deposits, in turn, grade into floodplain silts which are deposited in a backwater reach caused by the next fan downriver.

The discharges of the Alexandra and North Saskatchewan Rivers vary daily and seasonally in a cyclic pattern. Cirque and outlet glaciers from the Columbia Icefield provide water for the high daily discharges during summer. The annual peak discharge occurs during summer and averages 140 m^3s^{-1} (5800 cusecs). Night-time discharges are about half of the high flow during the previous day. From hydrographs of the Saskatchewan Crossing station between 1950 and 1970 and interviews of local residents, no evidence was found to indicate that "jokulhlaups" (glacial water outbursts) have occurred in the last 75 years. Of the total discharge, approximately 60% is carried by the Alexandra River, with the upper North Saskatchewan contributing the remaining 40% (data from three temporary gauging stations; 1969-71).

PROCESSES OF AGGRADATION

Aggradation on Primary Fans

Following the recession of Wisconsinan Ice from the area
about 9000 years B.P. (Westgate and Dreimanis, 1967), tributary
streams were likely to have rapidly eroded the lateral moraine
which dammed side valleys, thus depositing alluvial fans on the
floor of the Saskatchewan Valley. It is reasonable to conclude that
the readily available supply of till would diminish with time, causing
the growth rate of the fans to wane. Evidence of this consists of a
layer of volcanic ash exposed in stream cuts. This has been identified as Bridge River ash, dated at 2400 ± 200 years B.P. (Westgate
et al, 1971), and buried only 1 to 1-1/2 m (3 to 5 ft) beneath the
surface of the Rampart Creek fan.

In contrast, the primary fan of the North Saskatchewan
is still actively aggrading. Trunks of several standing trees on the
fan are buried to depths up to 1-1/4 m (4 ft) by gravel. During
periods of high discharge, large quantities of coarse sediment are
transported as bedload, much of which never leaves the fan after
deposition. The source of the gravel, located 19 km (12 mi) upriver,
consists of active outwash from the Saskatchewan Glacier and
terraces of old outwash currently being eroded.

Aggradation of the Main River - Backwater Reaches

A detailed survey of the longitudinal profile of the
Alexandra-North Saskatchewan River surface confirms the presence
of two primary fans deposited by Rampart Creek and North
Saskatchewan River (cf. Figure 2). It is proposed that secondary

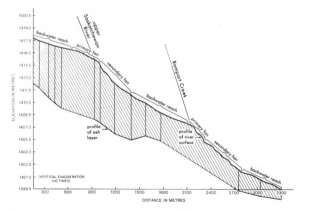

Figure 2 - Graph showing the long profile of
the Alexandra-North Saskatchewan River.

aggradation features occur both upriver and downriver from the periphery of the two deposits. A reach of bottom-land affected by back water extends upriver from both of the fans, while downriver, secondary fan processes occur.

Lateral deposition has forced the main river to flow between the periphery of the fan and adjacent valley side, constricting the channel and raising local base level to produce backwater. Backwater effects were confirmed by computation of backwater curves which fit closely the heights of levees above the channel bed. Levee heights decrease upriver to a transition zone where the backwater meets a secondary fan. Backwater effects become significant at discharges near 165 m^{3}s^{-1} (5800 cusecs). Channels are then at bankfull stage, while some levees are topped by overbank flooding. Further increases in discharge and flooding will increase deposition in backswamps, floodponds and levees. At bankfull discharge, several samples of suspended load averaged 9000 ppm, most of which consisted of silt and fine sand; the same size range of sediment was found in levee and backswamp deposits.

Aggradation in backwater levees and swamps was confirmed by the discovery of silts, wood, and other organic matter to depths of 7-1/2 m (25 ft). The main aggradation processes consist of overbank flooding and accumulation of vegetal matter, with the latter processes particularly active in backswamps. The volume of organic litter in levee and backswamp sediments varies between 7 and 98%.

Frost heaving plays a minor and indirect role in increasing the height of backwater levees. Frost heave-mounds are up to 1-1/4 m (4 ft) above the levee surface, 1/2 to 3 m (2 to 10 ft) in diameter, and form beneath woody material, usually trees or willows.

Drill hole sediment samples also suggest the occurrence of aggradation in channel beds in the backwater reach. In most straight channels the drill penetrated 6-1/2 m (21 ft) of silt and fine sand on both sides of the channel. However, in meanders more than 1 m (3 ft) of silt was found overlying point bar gravels, whereas silt deposits to depths greater than 6-1/2 m (21 ft) were found in the meander erosion bank. Results from stratigraphy revealed in drill holes indicates remarkable stability of straight channels, while meanders show evidence of lateral migration (cf. Figure 3).

Aggradation on Secondary Alluvial Fans

Downriver from the channel contractions, further gravel aggradation occurs where the river is free to braid and shift its channel laterally. The slope on these secondary fans is sufficiently steep for rivers to flush away any recent accumulations of silt or gravels. However, located among the fan gravels are stable islands of floodplain silts which continuously build up from annual flooding. The surfaces of the islands and channel gravels appear to be aggrading at equal rates.

The channel gravels are built up by bedload sediment transported and deposited as transverse gravel bars. Observations indicate that transverse bars form where the flow lines diverge and velocity decreases. The bars both thicken and lengthen downriver between the banks, forming a nearly flat topped deposit with a short but steep foreset slope on the downstream end. Such bars are later partially destroyed by downcutting and lateral erosion as flow and transport conditions diminish.

On the islands the main process of aggradation is over= bank flooding, aided by a thick growth of grass and shrubs, which retard the flow and allow deposition of silt. A second process of island up-building is the accumulation of plant roots. In samples of island silts the volume of roots in sediment averaged 16%.

Vegetation also assists in retarding bank erosion by reinforcing the cohesiveness of the sediment and providing a thick root mat flanking the islands, affording protection from severe fluvial erosion. Erosion tests of natural bank samples were carried out in a shear box submerged in the river. For the tests a mean river velocity of 1.6 m s^{-1} (5.2 ft s^{-1}) was used. Silt sized particles made up 70% of the sediment distribution. Erosion tests were conducted on silts without vegetation, silts with root reinforcement, and silts with both root reinforcement and a 2 in (5cm) thickness of root riprap. Comparison of erosion rates on a relative basis shows that silts with root reinforcement are about 600 times more resistant than silts without roots, and that silts with root reinforcement and riprap are 20,000 times more resistant than silts alone. Rates of erosion for the three bank materials, silts, silts with root reinforcement, and silts with root reinforcement and riprap averaged 265 kgm/hr (582 lbs/hr), 0.55 kgm/hr (1.2 lbs/hr), and 0.014 kgm/hr (0.03 lbs/hr), respectively.

These results compare favorably with erosion rates measured from pins inserted into natural channel banks composed of the same material. They suggest that vegetation plays the major role in the survival and aggradation of silt islands in the zone of secondary fans.

AGGRADATION RATES

Rates of aggradation were determined from buried trees and volcanic ash and were found to vary with respect to distance from primary fans. One method used to estimate rates of aggradation was to measure the burial rate of living trees. Fourteen trees growing in sand or gravel sites were selected for dating. Such sites are well drained and show no signs of frost heaving. Ages of the trees were determined by coring and ring counts. Burial depth of the tree trunk was measured from the present ground surface down to the root collar. It is assumed that the root collar corresponds to the ground surface at the time of germination. The oldest tree measured was 358 years old. It was buried by 119 cm (47 in) of sediment showing a deposition rate of 1 m in 290 years (1 ft in 93 yrs).

Aggradation rates were also computed from the thickness of alluvium above a thin layer (6 to 12 mm, or 1/4 to 1/2 in) of volcanic ash, which was encountered at depths ranging from 1.2 to 7.5 m (4 to 25 ft) (cf. Figure 2) in 80% of the holes drilled. This ash, which has been identified as Bridge River ash and dated by Westgate et al (1970) is also exposed in river banks down valley from the study area.

Aggradation rates during the last 2400 years, based on the ash layer, vary between 1 m in 1488 years (1 ft in 480 yrs) in the downriver part of the study area to 1 m in 300 years (1 ft in 96 yrs) in the upper reach. A comparison of data from both the buried tree and ash methods shows that aggradation rates from the tree method were always greater, which suggests that deposition rates may be increasing. Recent glacial activity may account for the increased rate of aggradation.

The changes in thickness of alluvium above the ash layer indicate that aggradation is controlled by primary fans. Figure 2 shows thinning wedges of post-Bridge River alluvium extending upriver (Alexandra) and downriver from the North Saskatchewan primary fan. This trend suggests that the presence of primary fans directly affects the morphology of secondary fans and back-water reaches.

CHANNEL PATTERN

Four different channel patterns occur in the study area and each occurs in a specific aggradational environment (cf. Figure 4). Within each depositional environment, channels with fan, contracted, braided and multi-meandering patterns can be recognized and related to river gradient and bank material.

Fan-shaped channel patterns, characterized by steep gradients in non-cohesive, coarse gravels, have formed on both primary fans. The gradient of the Saskatchewan fan averages 6.6 m. km-1 (35 ft. mi⁻¹). Eighty-four % by weight of the gravel particles is greater than 4 mm in diameter and some have diameters up to 100 mm. As a result of steep gradients in such non-cohesive bank material, rivers easily erode their banks laterally, forming numerous, shallow and nearly straight channels.

Contracted channels have formed between the toe of primary fans and adjacent valley-side slopes. Constricted channels have been unable to migrate laterally because of large gravels and boulders up to two feet in diameter in the banks. Such coarse sediment was transported across the fans by floods and washed out of glacial tills which flank the valley floor. Gradients of the contractions vary, depending on rate of aggradation downriver. The slope of the contraction caused by the Saskatchewan fan has a continuous gradient of 1.4 m· km⁻¹ (7.4 ft· mi⁻¹). In the Rampart fan-induced contraction, the channel slope steepens, because of the slow rate of aggradation downriver. The slow deposition rates downriver reflect the small volume of bedload sediment contributed by Rampart Creek and North Saskatchewan River.

Braided channels with extensive lateral oscillations are characteristic patterns on secondary fans. The slope of braided channels averages 2.2 m. km⁻¹ (11.6 ft. mi⁻¹), as compared to 6.5 m.km⁻¹ (34 ft. mi⁻¹) for fan channels. Sieve analysis of gravel showed 84% of the sediment by weight to be greater than 1 mm in diameter, with the largest pebbles measuring 40 mm. The decrease in both gradient and particle size with increased meander oscillations of channels, when compared with fan channels, suggests that the three characteristics are related. This relationship is even more pronounced in meanders in the backwater reach (Figure 4).

Multi-meandering channel patterns dominate the backwater reaches. These channels have low gradients and meander through thick accumulations of floodplain deposits. Gradients of meanders in the lower Alexandra backwater average 0.55 m· km⁻¹ (2.9 ft, mi⁻¹), and 0.97 m. km⁻¹ (5.1 ft. mi⁻¹) in the North Saskatchewan backwater. In the thick floodplain deposits, bank erosion is markedly reduced by fine sediment with grains less than 1 mm in diameter, and accumulations of plant roots, which average 18% of the total sediment volume. In the upper backwaters, the braided channels converge into several meanders, with large oscillations. In the lower backwaters the large meanders converge into a single channel, contracted by primary fans.

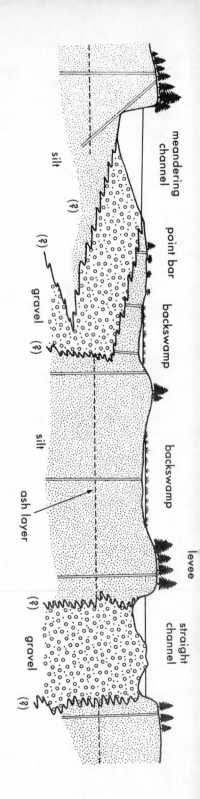

Figure 3 – Cross-sectional sketch of alluvial stratigraphy located at the first drill hole site upriver from the Rampart Creek fan.

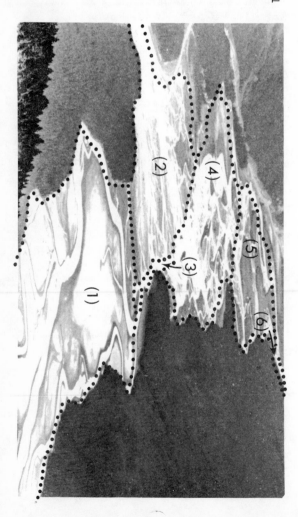

Figure 4 –

View looking downriver over the study area. Photo shows a complete sequence of depositional environments and channel patterns. Located in the lower right are (1) multi-meandering channels in the Alexandra backwater, (2) the Saskatchewan fan, (3) induced channel contraction, (4) the channel braids on the secondary fan, (5) multi-meanders in the Saskatchewan backwater, and (6) the Rampart fan-induced channel contraction.

The foregoing discussion suggests that channel pattern characteristics, channel numbers per valley cross-section, and meander width are related to bank cohesiveness and channel gradient. Channel bank cohesiveness, a function of sediment particles size and vegetation, is considered to be the main cause for the size of meanders. Bank cohesiveness is also regarded as the chief determinant of the number of channels per valley cross-section; the coarser the sediment the more numerous the channels. Channel gradient, which partly controls flow velocity, indirectly controls particle size distribution of sediment. On the other hand, larger sediment sizes in the channels act to increase the roughness and to reduce velocity. This presents a classical problem: which variable, gradient or sediment size, regulates channel pattern? Furthermore, it is a fact that aggradation processes and vegetation play a major role in preserving floodplain deposits and establishing gradient. The writer believes that channel pattern is related to a combination of variables, the most important being aggradation, channel gradient, particle size distribution of sediment, and vegetation.

Chapter 4-6

OBSERVATIONS ON SEDIMENTATION AT LILLOOET DELTA, BRITISH COLUMBIA.

R. Gilbert*

While literature on delta building and deltaic sequence is extensive, the processes of sediment distribution at the mouths of relatively high energy, glacial sediment laden streams as found throughout the Coast Mountains of British Columbia remains relatively uninvestigated. This report presents preliminary results of study on a large fresh water delta in the Lillooet River drainage, the major river basin in the south Coast Mountains.

Lillooet Lake, 147 km (92 mi) from the head of the basin, serves as an effective trap for large loads of glacial sediment transported by Lillooet River and its major tributary, Green River, together draining 3100 km^2 (1200 mi^2) (Figure 1). Birkenhead River (draining 600 km^2; 230 mi^2) also flows to the head of Lillooet Lake but contributes much less sediment to delta building. Less than 1% of Birkenhead Basin is presently glacierized as compared with 8 to 10% of Lillooet-Green Basin. Records of discharge, available for varying periods from 1914, indicate mean annual discharges of 126, 48 and 24 m^3 sec^{-1} (4500, 1700 and 850 cu sec) for Lillooet, Green and Birkenhead Rivers respectively. Daily mean flow in Lillooet River below Green River varies from 36 m^3 sec^{-1} (1275 cu sec) in February to over 400 m^3 sec^{-1} (14,000 cu sec) in June and July. The highest discharges are occasionally associated with autumn rains. For example, on October 19, 1940 Lillooet River reached 900 m^3 sec^{-1} (32,000 cu sec) and Green River reached 400 m^3 sec^{-1} (14,000 cu sec), the greatest recorded discharges. Although these floods are generally short lived, they may significantly affect the movement of sediment on the delta.

DELTA MORPHOLOGY

Subaerial

The first map of the delta was produced by the Royal

*The financial support of the National Research Council of Canada is gratefully acknowledged.

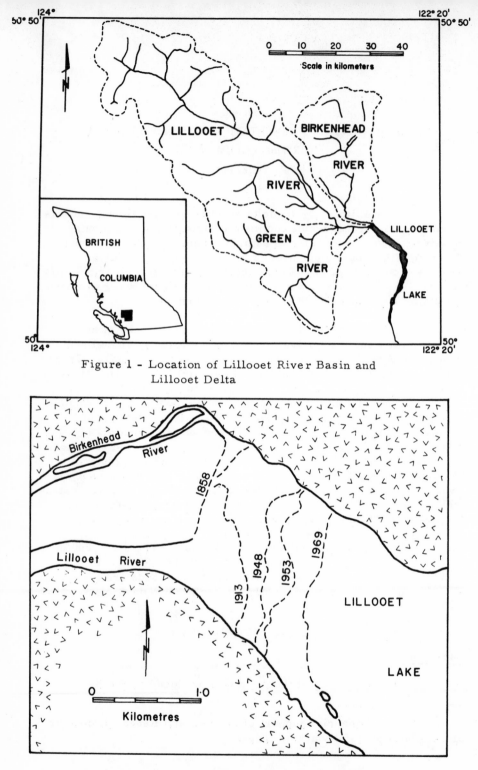

Figure 1 – Location of Lillooet River Basin and
Lillooet Delta

Figure 2 – Advance of Lillooet Delta between
1858 and 1969, plotted from official
surveys and air photography.

Engineers in 1859. Accurate large scale mapping of the delta was carried out in 1913 and 1945. From these maps and from frequent air photo coverage beginning in 1948, the rate of delta advance (mapped in Figure 2) was determined as given in Table I. The sharp increase after 1948 is probably associated with the steepening of the river gradient when Lillooet Lake was lowered 2.5 m in 1952 and with the major dyking and straightening program carried out on the river in this period as well as with agricultural clearing and logging in the watershed (see paper by Slaymaker, Section 5).

TABLE I

Rates of Lillooet Delta Advance Between
1858 and 1969

Period	Mean frontal advance m yr^{-1}
Summer 1858 - October 1913	7
October 1913 - October 1, 1948	8
October 1, 1948 - May 23, 1953	30
May 23, 1953 - July 19, 1969	21

As the active delta surface, which extends 1.6 km (1 mi) upstream from the delta front, is several metres below that of the flood plain, it is completely flooded every year. From the early maps and the air photograph coverage (e.g. Figure 3), it can be seen that during moderate and low flow there is a number of rapidly shifting distributaries of which the principal is most commonly found on the south side of the delta.

Subaqueous

From echo sounding surveys, the subaqueous delta deposits can be divided into four genetically distinct zones on the basis of slope and surface features.

1)   The first zone is the upper slopes, which are probably foreset beds in the classical sense. Coarser material that makes up the bed load is dropped here directly from the river in beds that dip forward at angles near the subaqueous angle of repose. The thickness of this zone is small in comparison to the ones below, seldom exceeding 6m. (20 ft.)

2)   At approximately 8 m (26 ft) depth there is a sharp break of slope to the second zone, which extends to about 90 m (295 ft) depth. Slopes vary from 3.6° to 5°, generally decreasing downslope. The slope above 20 m (65 ft) depth is

189

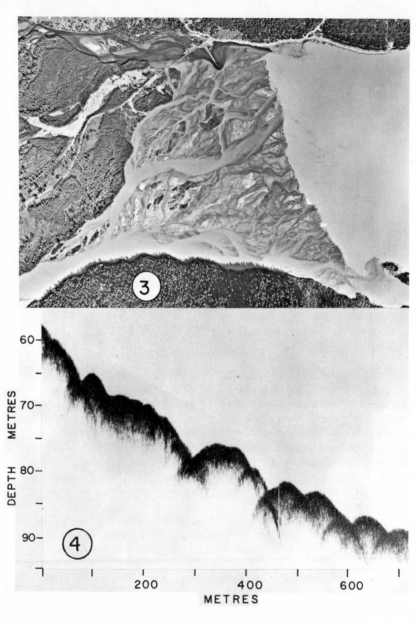

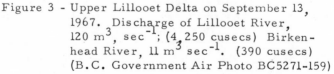

Figure 3 - Upper Lillooet Delta on September 13,
1967. Discharge of Lillooet River,
120 m^3, sec^{-1}; (4,250 cusecs) Birkenhead River, 11 m^3 sec^{-1}. (390 cusecs)
(B.C. Government Air Photo BC5271-159)

Figure 4 - (lower) Echogram of slumped sediment
deposits on the foreset beds of Lillooet
Delta. For location of transect, see
figure 5.

relatively smooth. Below this depth there is a series of irregular mounds, increasing in height down slope from 1 to 2 m (3 to 7 ft) to 7 m (23 ft) or more (Figure 4).

3)   The third zone, between approximately 90 and 120 m (295 and 390 ft) depth, is distinguished from the second principally by a decrease in slope to 1.4° to 2.4°. Large irregular mounds cover the entire surface but end abruptly at a break of slope marking the beginning of the fourth zone.

4)   The upper part of the fourth zone, extending to the constriction caused by the delta of Ure Creek (Figure 5), is nearly featureless and has the lowest slope (0.2°). At the lip of this constriction the slope steepens to 0.6° and a series of mounds several tens of metres long and less than a metre high can be seen on the echograms. Below 130 m (420 ft) depth the slope decreases slowly and the bottom is virtually featureless except for occasional mounds of material interpreted as slump deposits from the valley sides. In this area up to eight reflecting horizons in the upper 6 to 8 m (20 to 26 ft) of sediment can be seen on the echograms.

PRODELTA SEDIMENTS AND THEIR DISTRIBUTION

During a sampling program in 1970 fifty lake bottom and eight fluvial samples were taken with an Ekman grab sampler. The results of grain size analysis are summarized in Figure 6. The fluvial sediments (group 3) are distinct from the lacustrine sediments, indicating that virtually all of the coarse sand and gravel is trapped in the foreset beds of zone 1.

The mounds of zones 2 and 3, illustrated in Figure 4, indicate strongly that slumping is a major factor in redistributing sediments on the delta front. The phenomenon has been observed to be significant on other deltas (i.a. Terzaghi, 1956; Mathews and Shepard, 1962; Houbolt and Jonker, 1968; and Fulton and Pullen, 1969). Little is known yet about the frequency of slumping on the front of Lillooet Delta. A large slump probably occurred on August 5, 1971 after a long period of high discharge and particularly heavy sediment inflow. It generated a wave approximately 0.5 m (1.6 ft) high and showed up on a continuous near-bottom temperature recording (see below) as a wave of warmer water. Periodic echo sounding surveys throughout the summer of 1971, during and after the period of maximum discharge, did not show any other major readjustment of the slump mounds.

A number of authors have stressed the importance of turbidity currents in the distribution of sediment in deltas. In an

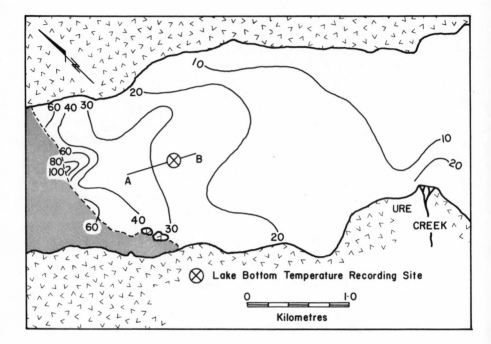

Figure 5 - Map of geometric mean grainsize, in
microns, of lacustrine sediments,
June, 1970. Transect AB refers to
echogram course of figure 4.

attempt to trace the movement of river water in the lake continuous
records of lake water temperature were kept 2 to 3 m (6 to 10 ft)
from the lake bottom at a site 1.0 km (0.6 mi) from the delta
(Figure 5) from July to September, 1971. In addition, vertical
profiles of temperature from surface to bottom at this site were
taken at regular intervals between May, 1970, and September,
1971. During spring and into summer a strong thermocline
develops at approximately 40 m (130 ft) depth; water temperature
below this depth remains relatively constant at 4° to 5°C. In 1971,
however, during periods of heavy sediment discharge, river water
passed along the bottom in regular waves lasting for several days
(Figure 7a), or in shorter bursts lasting for several hours at the
peak of sediment inflow each day (Figure 7b and c). This underflow
caused considerable warming of the bottom water and even the
disappearance of the thermocline on several occasions. During
July and August, 1971, temperature fluctuations indicating the

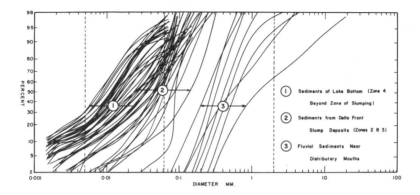

Figure 6 - Cumulative grainsize distributions of
lacustrine sediment samples, June,
1970.

passage of warmer river water occurred 86% of the time with
major fluctuations (for example those of Figure 7) occurring 37%
of the time. Thus, during times of heavy sediment inflow, turbidity
currents are probably a very significant factor in the distribution of
fluvial sediment. The grainsize of bottom sediments (Figure 6)
corresponds well with that of the turbidity current deposits of
Lake Mead (Smith et al, 1960) and the bottom slopes are sufficient
to maintain turbidity current flow (Bell, 1942) even in the flattest
areas. During 1970, a year of lesser sediment inflow, there was
no evidence of warming of the water below the thermocline and
bottom temperatures remained close to 4°C.

CONCLUSION

            Preliminary studies of Lillooet River Delta at Lillooet
Lake indicate that large loads of glacial and flood plain derived
sediment are distributed in the lake principally by means of
slumping and turbidity current flow. Fluvial gravel and coarse
sand are deposited at the river mouth in steeply dipping beds which
build outward over the slump deposits below. Slumps occur infre-
quently but are responsible for the removal of major masses of
sediment to the deeper parts of the lake. During periods of high
sediment inflow turbidity currents of river water pass along the
lake bottom, sometimes continuously for several days. These

currents provide a means for transport of large volumes of medium
and fine grained sediment far beyond the delta front.

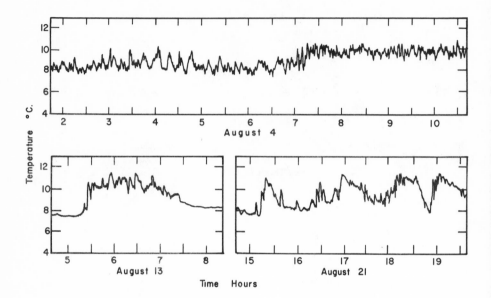

Figure 7 - Continuous temperature record traces
at 78 m (260 ft.) depth 1 m (3.3 ft.)
from bottom, 1971. For location of
recording site, see figure 5.

SECTION FIVE

ENVIRONMENTAL MANAGEMENT
OF MOUNTAIN REGIONS

Chapter 5-1

WATER QUANTITY AND FLOW REGIME-
INFLUENCES OF LAND USE, ESPECIALLY FORESTRY.

B. C. Goodell

All forms of land use that alter the vegetative cover or change the physical characteristics of the soil influence the quantity of liquid water yield from the area or its distribution in time or both. In briefest terms, these effects on water outflow result from changes in the quantity of water vapour loss to the atmosphere and from changes in water detention on and within the earth mantle.

Urbanisation of an area, with its reduction of water consuming vegetation and its creation of earth surfaces that are impervious to water entry, represents a form of land use of greatest influence in increasing the quantity of water yield and the temporal variability of its flow. A mature, climax forest represents a land condition at the other end of a scale of decreasing quantity of water yield per unit of land area and decreasing flow variability. Implicit in this comparison is that the ambient climatic and physiographic environments (exclusive of edaphic factors) are the same on the two areas, or, conceptually, the forested area is urbanised.

Because forests, and especially commercially valuable forests, dominate the economically useful and intensively used lands of the coastal mountains of British Columbia, this paper will be largely devoted to discussing the impacts of forest harvesting and culture on water yield quantity and flow regime.

INFLUENCES ON WATER QUANTITY - THEORY

The quantity of water yield from a land area is the residual of precipitation input and evpotranspirative output.

Precipitation Input

It is generally assumed that neither vegetation nor changes in vegetation affect the gross input of precipitation at the level of a plane just above the vegetative canopy surface. This has never been proved conclusively, is still questioned occasionally but, in this paper, will be considered true. It is particularly subject to question with respect to coastal forests where coalescence of fog and low cloud droplets on foliage and subsequent drip

197

(occult precipitation) is possible and has sometimes been shown to
be significant in quantity. Ekern (1964) found in the Hawaiian
Islands that such precipitation amounted to 750 mm (30 in) annually.
Fogs and forest level clouds are common along the coast of British
Columbia as well as that of northwestern United States and Alaska
but few measurements of fog and cloud drip have been reported.
A brief study of only 18 weeks in a dense coniferous stand on the
Oregon coast indicated a fog drip input of 280 mm (11 in)
(Kittredge, 1948). Such precipitation along the British Columbia
coast seems to have gone unmeasured. It may be that occult
precipitation produced by the coastal forests serves significantly
to compensate for the evapotranspiration by these forests but no
estimation of such compensation is possible.

Evapotranspiration

The influences of land use on evapotranspiration result
from effects on: (1) the energy supply potentially available for
water vaporisation, and (2) the availability of water to this energy
supply. Changes in vegetative cover can affect both of these factors
and so influence water yield quantity.

Under equivalent ambient conditions, the net input of
radiant energy of all wavelengths has been measured by Baumgartner
(1965) to be greatest into coniferous forests, less into grasslands,
and markedly still less into bare soil. The same author states that
deciduous forests stand between coniferous forests and grasslands
along this scale and that canopy roughness is similarly ranked
among the four categories of ground cover. This means that the
total energy supply, radiant plus convective, has the same
decreasing gradient among the four categories.

From bare soil, having the coarse texture common to
mountain lands, the soil water to a depth of only a few cm is
significantly available to the supply of energy for vaporisation. By
extending to greater depths and by their water extractive function,
plant roots increase the amount of soil water available to the
evaporation process. Tree roots, with their generally greater
depths of soil penetration, are more effective than the roots of
lesser vegetation.

A second way by which vegetation increases the
availability of water for evaporation is through its canopy interception of precipitation and a retention of a portion of it until lost
by vaporisation. It could be argued that this water of interception
would be as freely available if it impinged on the soil surface, was
absorbed, and, as soil water, became subject to evaporation and
transpiration. Such argument is invalid for two reasons:

198

(1) intercepted water is more freely exposed to radiative and convective energy and to conditions conducive to the maintenance of strong gradients in vapour pressure, and (2) intercepted water is not subject to the stomatal resistance to which water of transpiration is subject. This resistance is inherent in the diffusion pathway that transpired water must follow through the substomatal cavity and through the very small diameter tube that constitutes the stomate itself (Lee, 1967). Transpiration is subject to stomatal resistance plus boundary layer resistance whereas the evaporation of intercepted water is subject to the latter only.

A more valid argument against the hydrologic significance of interception is that transpiration is necessarily reduced while evaporation of the interception water is taking place. The latter is only partially compensatory, however, because of the greater resistance to transpiration that is pointed out above. Rutter (1968) concludes that, because of this difference in resistance, the degree of compensation on a forested site and at an air temperature of 24°C is likely to be on the order of 30% of the amount of intercepted water, i.e. the net loss of water is equal to 70% of the rainfall retained on the forest canopy. His comparable estimate for a grassed area is 20% of the intercepted and retained water.

INFLUENCE ON WATER QUANTITY - OBSERVED

The quantitative assessment of land surface cover effects on water yield quantity is problematic in the mountainous coastal area of British Columbia and similar topographically rough areas. Every watershed (catchment) is inherently a mosaic of multitudinous areas differing in the magnitudes of the factors effective on energy supply as well as water availability. Instrumentation for measurement of all significant factors at even a point in space are not available and, if available, the cost of adequate sampling would be prohibitive.

It may be fairly stated that the only conclusive data on the consumption of water by forests are those obtained from small watersheds where both precipitation input and total streamflow output have been intensively measured. The same statement may be made with respect to the effects on water yield resulting from forest reduction through complete or partial harvesting.

A sizeable body of such data has been collected from watersheds scattered throughout the world and representative of a variety of climate and vegetation complexes (Hibbert, 1965). For coastal British Columbia, such data are currently non-existent but have been derived from research in the coastal mountains of Oregon where climate and forest cover make the data germane to the southern coast of British Columbia.

In the Cascade Mountains of Oregon, where annual precipitation averages 2290 mm (90 in) (as measured in forest-free areas) a watershed of 0.96 km^2 (0.37 mi^2) was completely cleared of a dense stand of old growth Douglas Fir and all remaining foliage was destroyed by burning. Annual water yield responded with an annual increase equivalent to 460 mm (18 in) of water depth over the watershed area (Rothacher, 1970). From another, similar watershed in the same area the complete clearing of trees and lesser vegetation from 30% of the watershed resulted in immediate annual increases of about 150 mm (6 in).

If occult precipitation is assumed to be zero on both the Oregon area and on the British Columbia coast, then the above data may be considered indicative of the water consumed and lost to streamflow by a forest representative of the latter area. It is not representative, however, of the effects of commercial logging of forests from larger watersheds where management is for the sustained yield of timber. Under sustained yield management as currently practiced locally, the interval between successive timber harvests on the same, specific area of land is about 100 years. This means that approximately only 1% of a watershed is cleared of forest each year.

Re-growth of forests is rapid on coastal lands and a similarly rapid increase in water use by the new forest is to be expected. Rothacher (ibid.) estimates that the initial gain of 460 mm (18 in) will decline logarithmically to zero in 20 years. Thus over a 20 year period after logging, the average annual value of the increase will be only about 100 mm ((4 in) and this will be relevant to only 80% of the whole area of the watershed. It follows then, that for a large catchment that is under management for the sustained yield of timber, the average annual increase in water yield caused by forest clearcutting will be approximately only 20 mm (0.8 in) or 1.5% of the average annual pre-logging streamflow of 1370 mm (54 in) realized from the Oregon watershed.

Forests and thus forest removal also affect the seasonal distribution of streamflow quantity. Of the water yield increase from the Oregon watershed where there was complete forest removal, 80% occurred during the October-March rainy period and only 20% during spring and the dry summer months.

Although the summer increase was small in absolute quantity, it was large in relation to the pre-logging yield for this season. Thus a measured increase of 3.8 mm (0.15 in) in September represented a 150% increase over the 2.5 mm (0.1 in) of pre-logging yield for this month. If this increase is used to estimate the long-term average increase in September yield to be expected from sustained yield forest management, as was done above for annual quantity of streamflow, we derive an estimate of a 7% increase in the streamflow of this dry month. This compares with a 1.5% increase for the entire year.

INFLUENCES ON FLOW REGIME - THEORY

The factors by which land use affect flow regime (temporal characteristics of streamflow) may be grouped into 4 categories. One of these consists of the factors that affect the quantity of water stored within the earth mantle (regolith) of the watershed at a given time, for this storage affects the rate of input in a positive manner. These factors have already been covered through the discussion of the effects on water losses through water vaporisation. Water loss from storage to the atmosphere is directly translated into reduced rate of output of streamflow and into opportunity for storage of subsequent precipitation inputs. The other categories of factors effective on regime are: (1) the pathways by which rainfall or snowmelt water moves to natural stream channels, (2) snowmelt processes, and (3) the factors influencing the conveyance efficiency of these channels.

Pathways to Stream channels

Through the layers of organic debris that forests and other types of vegetative cover build up on mineral soil, the overland flow of incident water is minimized or prevented except when and where the mineral soil freezes to an impervious condition. This latter condition is believed to be of insignificant occurrence in the forested area of coastal British Columbia and so will not be discussed here.

In the local and undisturbed forests, overland flow seldom if ever occurs. The organic mat absorbs the impacts of raindrops, and prevents disintegration of the mineral soil surface with its accompanying sealing of the pores of this surface. The clean water reaching the mineral soil can be readily absorbed at rates greatly exceeding the maximum rates of rainfall or release of snowmelt water.

Forest harvesting may or may not result in significant overland flow. If the removal of logs is by aerial means (overhead cable or balloon) such that the logs are not dragged nor machines driven over the ground surface, then overland flow is unlikely even if burning over of the area follows the harvesting. The roads for log hauling are then the only surfaces of significant overland flow.

201

On the other hand, the movement of logs or machines over the area disrupts the organic layer to allow raindrop splash, and mineral soil sealing. Machines may also compact the mineral soil to reduce its capacity to accept water to below the rate of rainfall delivery. Both of these effects are conducive to overland flow. Moreover, both machines and logs are likely to create channels in which water collects and concentrates into flowing streams. The total result of all effects is more rapid delivery of water to natural channels and higher peak discharges.

Road networks may increase peak rates of discharge. To the effect of their impervious surfaces is added that of their drainage system which tends to augment the density of the natural stream system and increase delivery rates.

The mountain soils of coastal British Columbia are generally shallow, and, to the depth of tree rooting, contain numerous channels formed by root decay. These factors, combined with the normal steepness of slopes, operate to cause rapid movement of water through the soil mantle and to its interception by shallow, surface, drainage channels. Thus yield of water to stream channels is rapid but less so than if overland flow were common. Forest harvesting should increase the prevalence of root-hole channels but the influence on rate of water delivery is not known.

Snowmelt Processes

Forests retard the melting of snow by providing shade. By retarding air movement, they may also reduce the input of heat advected by the warm, moist air accompanying rainfall events. They may thus reduce peak discharge rates from the rain on snow events that are commin in coastal British Columbia. Snow held in forests until the late spring period of potentially high air temperatures and sunlight intensities can be hazardous in regions where clear weather melt is productive of floods but this situation is alien to coastal British Columbia.

Forest cutting generally augments snowmelt rates and tends to increase peak rates of streamflow for which snow is a source (Zinke, 1965). However, where forest cutting serves to cause relatively early snowpack dissipation from lower areas of coastal watersheds, it seems possible that peak rates may be reduced rather than increased.

Conveyance Efficiency of Channels

The over-mature forests that are still common in coastal
British Columbia present hazard to the conveyance efficiency of
natural stream channels. Large pieces of debris from these forests
often accumulate to cause damming of water courses. If the dams
are such as to be stable structures, they may cause but small
effects on flow regime. If such dams cause appreciable water
storage but are subject to being washed out during high flow events,
then they may serve to significantly augment such events on small
streams. In addition to affecting peak flows on creeks and minor
rivers, forest debris may cause local increase in stage or change
in channel location with resultant damage to raods and streamside
property.

As forest management for timber production continues,
this hazard will be reduced because the available quantity of debris
will be reduced. The first harvesting of local forests increases
the hazard, however, by causing a sudden great increase in forest
debris and often, through careless logging practices, a direct and
immediate input of debris into stream channels.

INFLUENCES ON FLOW REGIME - OBSERVED

For actual comparisons between the flow regimes of
streams from forested watersheds and watersheds disturbed by
logging activities, we are again dependent on Oregon studies.
Rothacher (1971) from observations made on the watersheds
previously referred to, drew the following conclusions:

> . . . under normal conditions, logging -- and I'm
> including clearcutting -- does not significantly increase
> major floods in the Douglas Fir area west of the crest
> of the Cascades. By 'normal conditions' I am including
> the usual light disturbance caused by logging which is
> not sufficient to decrease infiltration capacity of the soil
> below the rate of precipitation. That is there is no
> large-scale change from subsurface flow to surface
> flow. (p. 46)

One of the watersheds from which this conclusion was
substantially drawn was logged by means of an aerial cable
(Wyssen Skyline system) and with complete absence of roads.
Logging of the other "disturbed" watershed was by the high-lead
system, which is most common all along the Pacific coast, but
logging only extended over 30% of the watershed. The observations
included two major floods produced by heavy and prolonged rains

that thoroughly wetted the soils of both the forested (control) watershed and the completely logged and partially logged watersheds.

Rothacher (1971) also presents unpublished results (Gilleran, 1968; Harper, 1969; Hsieh, 1970) from the coastal mountains of Oregon that show significant increases in peak flows caused by roads alone and roads combined with logging. ". . . roadbuilding which altered 3 to 4% of the drainage had little influence on peak flows. When over 12% of the drainage was in roads, there was a significant increase in peak flows which was increased still further when 72% of the drainage was logged." (p. 5)

Local Research on Forest Influences

Under financing by the Greater Vancouver Water District and Federal agencies, a program of research into forest influences is currently being conducted by the Faculty of Forestry of the University of British Columbia in cooperation with the Departments of Soil Science and Geography. Initiated in 1969, this research has the three objectives of (1) adding to the existing, meagre knowledge of the hydrologic phenomena of undisturbed watersheds of the coastal mountains of British Columbia, (2) evaluating the hydrologic effects of forestry practices, and (3) determining how forestry practices can and should be modified to minimize influences detrimental to the water resource and, where possible, maximize influences that are beneficial. The research is sited in the Seymour and Capilano catchments -- two of the three major source areas of water for Metropolitan Vancouver (Figure 1). To the present, effort has been concentrated on field instrumentation and on relatively short term studies of soil water movement and the mass wasting of soil. Two of these studies are reported by Chamberlin and by O'Loughlin elsewhere in this volume. On Figure 1 are shown the more extensive networks of instrumentation and also the two experimental watersheds, on one of which -- Jamieson Creek watershed -- more intensive instrumentation is existent and planned.

Short and longer term balances between water inputs and outputs and between chemical inputs and outputs will be established for Jamieson Creek watershed under its current, pristine, forest cover and following the logging of the forest a few years hence. A more precise evaluation of logging effects on the quantity and regime of Jamieson Creek flow and on its chemical quality will be based on comparisons between Jamieson Creek and Elbow Creek prior to and after logging of the former.

The poorly defined boundaries of the watershed of Elbow Creek will prevent determination of water balances relevant to this

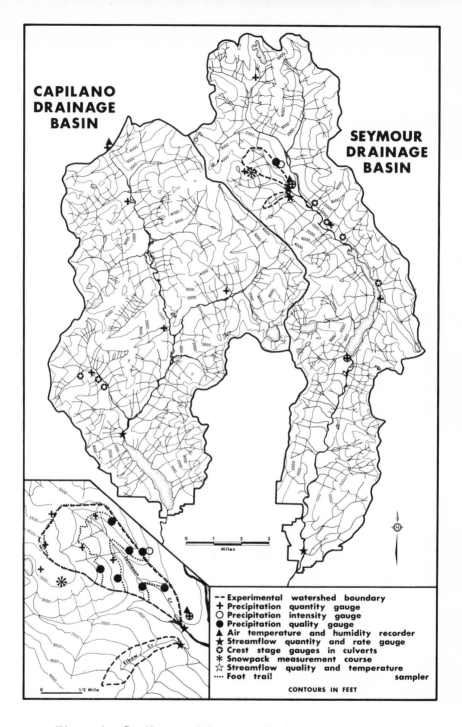

CAPILANO DRAINAGE BASIN

SEYMOUR DRAINAGE BASIN

-- Experimental watershed boundary
+ Precipitation quantity gauge
○ Precipitation intensity gauge
● Precipitation quality gauge
▲ Air temperature and humidity recorder
★ Streamflow quantity and rate gauge
⊕ Crest stage gauges in culverts
✳ Snowpack measurement course
☆ Streamflow quality and temperature
.... Foot trail   sampler

CONTOURS IN FEET

Figure 1 - Capilano and Seymour drainage basins
showing location of experimental
watersheds and field instrumental
sites.

area. This fact partially illustrates limitations on hydrologic research imposed by the immature and glaciated character of the mountains of coastal British Columbia. Another limitation is that the excessively steep gradients of most of the smaller streams render them unsuited to accurate gauging by conventional means. The choice of Elbow Creek as a stream comparable to Jamieson Creek was based on: (1) a channel reach suitable for accurate streamflow gauging, (2) stable, vegetative, watershed cover, (3) accessibility, (4) proximity to Jamieson Creek, and (5) non-existence of another stream having near equivalence in desiderata.

CONCLUSIONS

The use of land for wood production, through its inherent reduction of forest cover and evpotranspiration, results in the increase in quantity of water yield. In the coastal mountains of British Columbia, the annual increases associated with the commercial production of wood are likely to be of small economic significance. Increases in the low flows of summer may be of more importance to man's more direct use of water and also to fish populations. The regime variability of streamflow tends to be increased by land use for wood production that results in an extensive and dense network of roads and the extensive dragging of logs over the soil surface (ground skidding). This influence will be ameliorated as aerial movement of logs and an attendant reduction of road mileage become more common.

Chapter 5-2

A PREDICTIVE MODEL FOR SNOW STORAGE
IN THE TEMPERATE FOREST ZONE
OF THE COASTAL MOUNTAINS.

Ming-ko Woo

In winter, many river basins in the southern Coast
Mountains of British Columbia experience simultaneous snow
accumulation at higher altitudes and rain-on-snow melt at lower
altitudes. These processes give rise to a distinctive 'snow-line'
which marks the approximate elevation of the freezing level. Owing
to the changing position of the freezing level with different storms,
it is essential to budget the snowpacks by altitudinal zones in order
to predict basin streamflow and snow storage. An accurate evaluation of snow storage by altitudinal zones, however, requires a
sizable network of snow survey sites, whose maintenance may
prove to be uneconomical. Such a network is not available so the
writer has used a numerical simulation technique to assess snow
resources for small basins lying within the temperate forest
environment, and below the alpine zone. The temperate forest
belt covers an appreciable portion of the Coast Mountains (Figure 1)

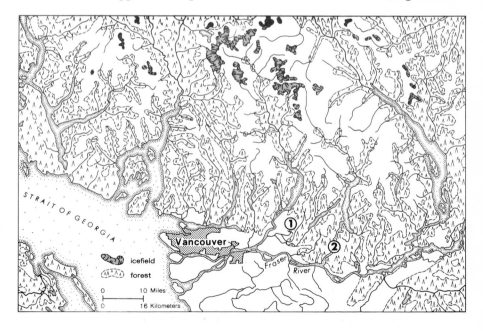

STRAIT OF GEORGIA

Vancouver

Fraser River

icefield

forest

① ②

0   10 Miles
0   16 Kilometers

Figure 1 - Location Map

and most of the major valleys have temperature and precipitation stations, some of which have been in operation for over 30 years. Data from such stations may serve as indicators of the weather conditions over the mountainous areas nearby. Hence, these stations are considered as 'base-stations' for the present simulation model.

THE SIMULATION MODEL

Spatial and Temporal Scales

Besides a division of the basin into altitudinal bands, each band is further distinguished in terms of two components: an open sector and a forest sector. This vegetational sub-division is necessary because of the practice of clear-cut logging which leaves behind open ground with a pattern of snow storage markedly different from that underneath the forest canopy. The present model simulates snow storage conditions at daily intervals for both forested and open sectors at various elevation bands.

Selection of Base-Station and Index Altitudes

Select a base-station with daily temperature and precipitation records. The station should not be too far away from the basin whose snow data are to be simulated. The median altitude of each elevation band is regarded as the index-altitude for the band.

Temperature

Maximum and minimum daily temperatures recorded at the base-station are then extended by lapse rates to the open sector of each band:

$$\theta_i = \theta_b - c(h_i - h_b) \tag{1}$$

where θ is daily maximum or minimum temperature
h is elevation
subscripts i and b refer to station i and the base-station respectively
c is an empirically derived lapse rate

Based on temperature in the open sector, temperature for the forest sector is computed by:

$$\theta_{f_i} = a + b\theta_i \tag{2}$$

where subscripts f_i and i refer to the forest and

open sectors of zone i
a and b are empirical constants

Precipitation

Precipitation at the base-station is extended to other elevations by an empirical relationship

$$P_i = P_b + k(h_i - h_b) \qquad (3)$$

where P is daily precipitation
h is elevation
k is an empirically determined constant

The amount of simulated precipitation is assumed to be an average condition for the entire elevation band. A probability matrix of snowfall and rainfall events (as conditioned by minimum daily temperature) is used to determine the minimum daily temperature at which snowfall occurs. The elevation band with this minimum temperature is considered to be the freezing level, and all zones below this level will have rain while those above it will receive snow. The amount of rainfall in the forest (or throughfall) is computed by:

$$P_{f_i} = rP_i \qquad (4)$$

where P_{f_i} is rainfall in the forest
P_i is rainfall in the open
r is an empirical coefficient

For snowfall, the amount reaching the forest floor is computed by:

$$P'_{f_i} = P'_i \qquad (5)$$

where P'_{f_i} is snowfall in the forest
P'_i is snowfall in the open
s is an empirical coefficient

Snowmelt

Snowmelt is distinguished into clear-weather melt and rain melt (U. S. Army, 1956). For the former type of melt,

$$M = m_1 \theta_{max}^2 \qquad (6)$$

where M is snowmelt
θ_{max} is maximum daily temperature
m_1 is an empirical coefficient

This is similar to the degree-day approach (Gartska et al, 1958) except that the relationship between melt and temperature is assumed to be non-linear.

For rain melt,

$$M = m_2 P \theta_{max} \qquad (7)$$

where P is daily rainfall
m_2 is an empirical coefficient

Snow Storage

Assuming little snow evaporation, the amount of snow storage for each sector is budgeted at daily intervals by computing the difference between the incoming snowfall and the outgoing snowmelt.

$$S_i = P_i' - M_i \qquad (8)$$

where S_i is the amount of snow storage at zone i
P_i' and M_i are the amounts of snowfall and snowmelt at zone i

To obtain numerical values for the various empirical equations, field observations were made at the University of British Columbia Research Forest at Maple Ridge, B. C. (1 in Figure 1). This model was then applied to a river basin where daily temperature and precipitation have been measured at a valley station for a long period.

RESULTS OF SIMULATION

A simulation run was performed on the IBM 360/67 computer at the University of British Columbia. Stave Falls, B. C. (2) was chosen as the base-station (Figure 1). This station is situated at a glaciated valley floor (elevation 60 m; 200 ft) and has been furnishing continuous daily records since 1928. Figure 2 shows the simulated snowpack conditions from a relatively severe (1968-69) and a relatively mild (1969-70) water year. During the mild winter, the snowpack at lower altitudes was not continuously maintained, but disappeared completely during periods of high temperature. At higher altitudes, however, the duration of snowpack remained similar in both the mild and the cold year. Melting of snowpacks at higher elevations proceeds rapidly and at a more uniform rate after May. On the other hand, at lower elevations, the rain-on-snow melt is more pronounced throughout winter, so that when spring comes, most areas are already devoid of snow.

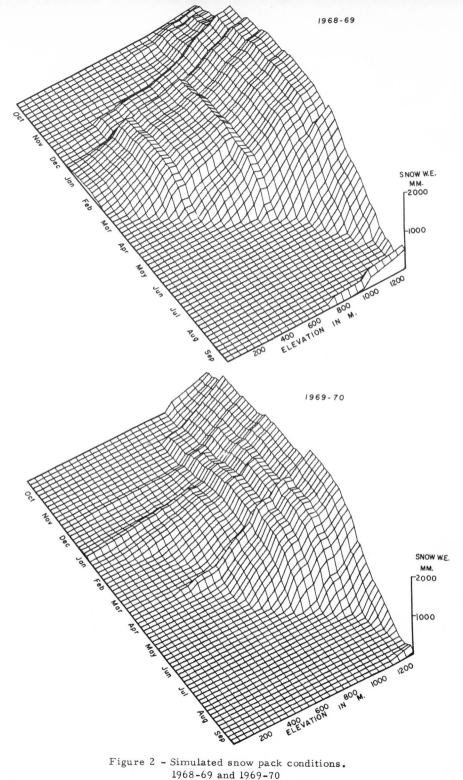

1968-69

1969-70

Figure 2 - Simulated snow pack conditions.
1968-69 and 1969-70

In terms of the management and the planning of water resources, it is more useful to examine the long-term patterns of snow storage. To demonstrate the reliability of the model for long-term prediction of snow storage, simulated records for the open sector at 1200 m (3940 ft) elevation for 1st April of each year were used to determine the probability that a given level of snow storage (in water equivalent units) is exceeded by the packs (Figure 3). Such records were then compared to 36 years of snow survey data available at Grouse Mountain, B. C. (1160 m; 3800 ft). A Kolmogorov-Smirnov test shows that their difference is not statistically significant. Hence, the model is considered to be satisfactory.

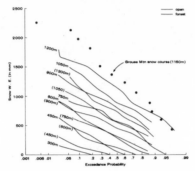

Figure 3 - Probability of snow storage in open
and forest sectors derived from
simulation model and checked
against Grouse Mountain snow
course data.

From the simulated records, the amount of snow storage in the open sector at the beginning of each month (from November to July) was found to be normally distributed.[1] In which case, the mean and the standard deviation are the parameters which would fully describe the long-term exceedance probabilities of snow storage. Figure 4 shows that for elevations below 800 m (2625 ft), larger standard deviations are associated with months with more snow. For higher elevations where snow storage is usually more substantial, snow storage varies greatly from year to year during the period May to June which corresponds with the melt season for such elevations. The diagrams also show that on the average, higher altitudes attain maximum snow storage at later dates than lower zones. The phenomenon corresponds with Schaerer's (1970)

------

[1]This is not to be confused with the maximum amount of snow on the ground which has been described by Thom (1966) as log-normally distributed.

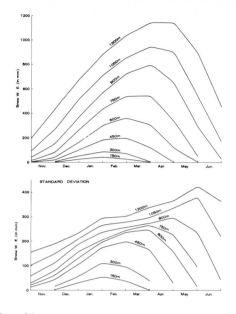

Figure 4 - Mean and standard deviation of
snow storage from simulation
model.

observation at a coastal mountain (Mount Seymour) that the highest
snow load occurs in January or early February in the valleys,
while it is attained in May for the elevation of around 1200 m
(3940 ft).

The amount of snow storage in the forest sector is less
than that in the open sector (Figure 3). The relatively thin pack
in the forest at lower elevations seems to be an important factor
for the snow to disappear earlier in the forest than in the open.
Another possible reason is the prevalence of rain-on-snow melt
during late winter which reduces the differential melt rate between
forest and open sites should clear-weather melt predominate.
Although most reports (e.g. Anderson et al, 1958; Meiman, 1968)
on snow storage under other types of forest environments show
that snow lasts longer under the canopy, field observations in the
temperate forest zone of the coastal mountains tend to support the
results of this simulation.

DISCUSSION

The main function of this model is to enable long-term
probabilistic predictions regarding the magnitude and duration of
snow storage at various elevations both inside the temperate forest
and   also   at the open sites. The model has been developed

213

primarily for a region where hydrometeorological data are scarce. This distinguishes the present model from other simulation models for snow hydrology which require more elaborate sets of data input (e.g. Anderson and Rockwood, 1970; Riley et al, 1969).

The logic of this model is readily adaptable to most areas of rugged terrain where the collection of snow information is expensive. All the empirical equations, however, were based on data from the Coast Mountains near Vancouver, B. C. When the model is applied to mountainous areas elsewhere, new sets of coefficients for the empirical equations must be derived.

The present model should by no means be considered as a substitute for snow surveys. Rather, with a combination of snow course data serving as a control on the model outputs, and the simulated data providing an estimate of the distribution of snow storage in small basins, it is hoped that a more realistic evaluation of water resources may be accomplished.

Chapter 5-3

TERRAIN AND VEGETATION OF SNOW AVALANCHE SITES
AT ROGERS PASS, BRITISH COLUMBIA.

P. A. Schaerer

The Division of Building Research of the National
Research Council of Canada is engaged in a study of snow avalanches
at Rogers Pass where the Trans Canada Highway crosses the
Selkirk Mountain range in British Columbia. The location was
chosen because numerous avalanches reach the valley every winter
and the control of them is an important part of the maintenance of
the highway.

The terrain and the climate at Rogers Pass are typical
for the mountains of the southern interior of British Columbia.
The elevation of the narrow valleys is between 900 and 1320 m
(2950 and 4350 ft) and the mountains rise to 3000 m (9850 ft) above
sea level. The average annual precipitation at Rogers Pass, at
elevation 1320 m (4350 ft), is 1.30 m (51 in); 0.80 m (32 in) of it
falls in the form of snow.

Avalanches start to slide at elevations of between 1500
and 2300 m (5000 and 7500 ft) and run out on the alluvial fans and
talus slopes in the valleys. Most avalanche site areas are between
50,000 and 200,000 m^2 (540,000 and 2,150,000 ft^2).

PROBLEM

Two of the objectives of the study are to obtain
information to facilitate identification of avalanche sites and to
estimate the magnitude and the frequency of occurrence of
avalanches from features of terrain and vegetation. The formation
of avalanches is the result of terrain factors such as slope and
ruggedness and is also influenced by the weather (e.g., snowfall,
wind, temperature). The various parameters are interrelated and
it is often difficult to isolate their influence.

The present studies are concerned with avalanches large
enough to be significant to traffic, to structures in their path, and
to hydrology, geomorphology, and forestry operations. Large
avalanches develop when the terrain and the snow condition in the
track below the starting point permit a large amount of snow to be
removed. There are many other small avalanches that are

significant only to avalanche hazard forecasting and skiing safety.

TYPES OF AVALANCHE TERRAIN

The three following characteristic types of terrain where avalanches develop can be found at Rogers Pass and in other areas of southern British Columbia.

Cliff

The important characteristic here is one or more steep outcrops of bedrock in a slope covered with loose rock, grass, or shrub (Figure 1). Snow starts to slide on or just below the steep parts of the terrain and then sets more snow into motion on the slope below. The rock outcrops have surface slope angles greater than 42° and in order for avalanches to grow to a large size the slope immediately below the starting point must have an incline of 28° or more. Cliff-type terrain can usually be recognized by its lack of vegetation and can be identified on black and white air photographs as horizontal bands in a light tone.

Gullies

Gully-type sites consist of a V-shaped main gully with numerous branches of steep-sided gullies (Figure 2). There is usually no well defined avalanche starting zone. Avalanches may start in any one of the gullies and, when descending into the main channel, set into motion the unstable snow on the steep gully sides.

The various side gullies often produce avalanches independently and at different times. Several avalanches may be observed at short intervals when weather conditions are favorable for their formation.

Lee Slopes

This type of terrain can be found on the leeward side of mountain ridges where large amounts of wind-transported snow are deposited (Figure 3). The slope need not have any steep sections, such as cliffs, but in order to produce large avalanches it would appear that the incline should be more than 28°. Avalanches usually fracture close to the ridge in the convex part of the slope just above the deepest accumulation of snow.

The 67 avalanche sites investigated at Rogers Pass could be categorized as follows: 36 cliff sites; 15 gully sites; 9 lee slope sites; 5 combinations of cliff and lee slope sites; and 2 combinations

Figure 1 - Cliff type site. Avalanches start to slide at
the two sharp drops of slope.

Figure 2 - Gully type avalanche site.

Figure 3 - Lee slope site. The direction of
the prevailing wind is from the
right-hand side; avalanches start
to slide on the slopes in the shade.

of gully and lee slope sites.

The cliff and lee slope avalanches are either funnelled
into a channel or may continue to slide over an open slope. The
gully type is by its nature associated with a channelled track.

INFLUENCE OF TERRAIN ON THE FREQUENCY
OF AVALANCHE OCCURRENCE

The number of times that avalanches will occur is
determined more by climate (i.e., frequency and magnitude of
snowfalls, temperatures that remain close to 0°C, and direction
and speed of wind) than by terrain characteristics. Conclusions
about how much terrain influences avalanche occurrence can only
be drawn in conjunction with the climate.

The slope incline appears to be the most important
parameter relevant to the frequency of occurrence of avalanches.
Other parameters are the shape of the track, its ruggedness,
vegetation cover, and exposure to wind and sun.

The avalanches close to the highway at Rogers Pass have
been recorded since 1953. In Figure 4 the average number of
medium and large size avalanches are plotted against the average

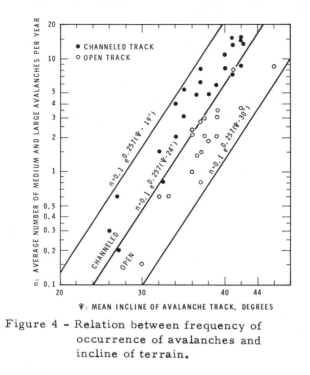

Figure 4 - Relation between frequency of
occurrence of avalanches and
incline of terrain.

slope angle of the avalanche track for the cliff-type and lee slope-
type sites. Gully sites could not be included in the analysis because,
at most of them, avalanches were controlled by artillery. Use of
artillery produces smaller, more frequent avalanches than would
occur under natural conditions. The incline was measured over
the full length of the track between the usual starting zone and the
beginning of the outrun zone, and the analysis included only those
avalanches that were large enough to run over the full length of
the track.

The graph shows that in order to produce large
avalanches a steeper incline is necessary on open slopes than in
channels such as valleys, gullies and troughs. One important
reason for the difference is that channels tend to have many small
avalanches and the snow deposited by them forms a smooth sliding
surface. Loup and Lovie (1967) also report a remarkable difference
in the frequency of avalanches between gullies and open slopes.

Exposure to wind and sun, variations of the incline,
ruggedness of the terrain and ground cover are responsible for the
scatter of the points in Figure 4. It is not yet possible to analyze
the influence of terrain characteristics. The method of slope
angle distribution, recommended by Strahler (1956), appeared to
be promising. The surface slope angles were determined with the

aid of topographic maps of scale 1:5000 and contour intervals 7.5 m (25 ft) for 40 to 100 random points in 34 avalanche sites. It was not possible, however, to establish a relation between the frequency and size of the avalanche and the variance of the slope angles. Avalanche activity appeared to be unrelated to the maximum slope or to the percentage of terrain steeper than a threshold angle, e.g., 42° which is the maximum angle of repose of talus. It was only the average slope angle of the track that correlated with the frequency of the avalanches.

From observations made over a twelve-year period it was found that avalanches lose speed on an open snow surface when the incline is less than 28°. They begin to deposit their snow when the talus slopes and alluvial fans of the outrun zones are flatter than this critical angle. Depending on the speed attained in the track, and their mass, avalanches may run much further and sometimes climb the opposite side of the valley.

TREE GROWTH AS AN INDICATOR OF AVALANCHE FREQUENCY

Avalanches have a significant destructive effect on forests. Their tracks can easily be recognized in the mountain area of southern British Columbia by the scars on heavily forested slopes. The dominant species of trees at Rogers Pass are Engelmann Spruce (Picea engelmanni), Western Hemlock (Tsuga heterophylla), and Western Red Cedar (Thuja plicata). Open areas in the forest are covered mainly with Mountain Alder (Alnus tenuifolia). The upper treeline is generally at the 2000 m (6600 ft) elevation.

The age of the trees in the outrun zones of avalanches is sometimes assumed to be equal to the number of years that have passed since the last large avalanche. This is true only for sites where avalanches happen so rarely that when one does occur large areas of mature timber are destroyed. At such sites seedlings begin to grow in the cleared area a year later and a young forest with numerous trees of equal age then appears. At sites with more frequent avalanches the trees are destroyed whenever they have reached a certain critical age and height; the result here is a growth of small trees with variable age.

A study of the height and age of trees in avalanche outrun zones was made at Rogers Pass and other areas. Such observations must be interpreted with caution, however, because not only avalanches but also soil conditions, climate, and exposure influence the growth of trees. Trees must be selected that are fully exposed to avalanches and not protected by boulders or a ridge of terrain. It should also be mentioned here that avalanches usually slide over the snow surface in the outrun zone and remove very little of the previously deposited snow.

The most interesting conclusion of the tree study was that it is the height rather than the age of the trees that determines how it reacts in avalanches; the reaction varies between the species. Height and age of trees are related however, e.g., the spruce trees at Rogers Pass grow at an average rate of 20 cm (8 in) per year, and the hemlocks at about 8 cm (3 in).

Engelmann Spruce is found most frequently in avalanche sites. Its chance for survival in avalanches is small when it is taller than 3.5 m (11.5 ft). Larger trees are usually broken or uprooted. Spruce trees shorter than 3.5 m (11.5 ft) are flexible enough to bend under the impact of the avalanche, and trees shorter than about 1.5 m (5 ft) are buried in the natural snow cover and are well protected.

Western Hemlock that are exposed to avalanches are usually broken near the snow surface, 1.2 to 2.0 m (4 to 6.5 ft) above ground. When the tree trunk does not break the trees are stripped of their needles and branches and then decline.

Western Cedar was found unsuitable as an indicator of avalanche activity, because of a great variation in the rate of growth and strength. Some cedars are observed to survive avalanches year after year and grow 8 m (26 ft) high and others, with equal exposure, break when they are only 3 m (10 ft) high.

Because spruce survives avalanches better and grows more rapidly than hemlock, forests at sites where avalanches have not occurred for 30 to 50 years contain mainly large spruce trees with only a few small hemlock trees. A stand of mixed spruce and hemlock of equal height and ages would indicate that no avalanches had reached its location for 100 or perhaps more years.

The studies on trees in avalanche sites enabled the following categories to be established:

(a)   Alder and willow brush (no coniferous trees higher than 1.5 m (5 ft). Large avalanches occur frequently, usually once per year.

(b)   Few large trees, no branches on the side facing the avalanche below 8 m (26 ft) above ground, few small trees. Avalanches occur once every one to three years. They produce mainly windblast and deposit snow not deeper than 1.0 m (3.3 ft).

(c)   No large trees and no dead wood from large trees;
spruce trees 3.5 to 4.5 m (11.5 to 15 ft) high and hemlock
1.5 to 2.0 m (5 to 6.5 ft) high, damaged branches and bark.
Large avalanches occur about once every three to ten years
and deposit deep snow.

(d)   Broken large trees and dense growth of small trees.
Large avalanches have occurred not more frequently than
once in ten years and probably not even once in thirty years.

CONCLUSION

Avalanche sites can be identified from features of
terrain and vegetation. There are numerous parameters that
determine the frequency of occurrence and the size of avalanches.
An idea of the average frequency of avalanches can be obtained
from the average incline of the avalanche track and the type and
height of trees in the outrun zone. General classifications could
be established for the Rogers Pass area and it is expected that they
could be extended to other areas in Western Canada.

Chapter 5-4

BEHAVIOR OF STEEP CREEKS IN A LARGE FLOOD.

S. O. Russell

On September 18, 1969, severe floods occurred on some of the very steep creeks which drain into Howe Sound in the Lions Bay area about 24 km (15 mi) north of Vancouver, British Columbia.

Although the floods were unusually high they were quite localised. The precipitation and stream gauging networks in the area are sparse, due to the mountainous nature of the terrain, and did not pick up any quantitative information on the magnitude or intensity of the rainfall which caused the floods. Despite the lack of reliable hydrologic data a comparison of the effects of the floods on the different creeks gave some useful qualitative information on the behaviour of steep creeks when subjected to very high discharges.

PHYSICAL SETTING

In the Lions Bay area the Coast Mountains rise steeply from Howe Sound to a height of more than 1200 m (4000 ft) within less than 2 km (about 1 mi). The terrain is rough with granitic and associated rock types at, or close to, the surface. Where bedrock is not at the surface, it is overlain with till or outwash sand, gravel and boulders. The slopes are forested except for some barren and very steep areas. The forest cover is typical Pacific coast rain forest, consisting mainly of Douglas Fir (Pseudotsuga mendiesii), Western Hemlock (Tsuga heterophylla) and Western Cedar (Thuja plicata). There has been some logging on the drainage basins of the creeks which flooded.

A road and a railway traverse the area parallel to the edge of the Sound. There has been limited housing development along the beach and more extensive development on the alluvial fan and along the lower reaches of Harvey Creek, the largest of the creeks affected by the flood.

The creeks which were subject to flooding are shown in Figure 1 and are listed in Table I.

223

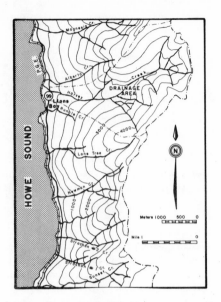

Figure 1 - Area of unusual flooding, on Howe
Sound, on September 18, 1969.
(Source, NTS 50,000 map No. 92G16 =
contours in feet).

TABLE I

DRAINAGE BASIN CHARACTERISTICS

Basin	Drainage Area	Average Slope
Harvey Creek	7.2 km^2 (2.8 mi^2)	32% (18°)
Lone Tree Creek	1.8 km^2 (0.7 mi^2)	60% (31°)
Newman Creek	2.0 km^2 (0.8 mi^2)	60% (31°)
Strachan No. 2 Creek	1.8 km^2 (0.7 mi^2)	60% (31°)

The cover on Harvey Creek drainage basin is approximately 40% forest, 42% barren, 14% logged and 4% being cleared
for development. Similar data are not available for the other
basins.

Lone Tree Creek flows over bedrock but the other three
creeks are mainly in overburden; their stream beds consist of
gravel and boulders to 1-1/2 m (5 ft) in diameter and occasional
rock outcrops. Except for Lone Tree Creek, the creeks have
gravel and boulder alluvial fans at their mouths indicating that the
creeks can move their beds during floods. Normally, however, the
water cascades between the rocks and boulders and is clear and

224

free from sediment.

FLOODS OF SEPTEMBER 18, 1969

There had been heavy rain in the whole area on
September 16 and 17 and the soil must have been saturated prior
to the flood. A low pressure area, stalled off the coast, spawned
convection cells which, aided by the orographic effect, produced
the intensive localised rainfall which caused the flooding.

The floods occurred in the early morning of September
18. The highway and railway bridges over Strachan No. 2 Creek
were washed away; debris was piled under and on top of the road
bridge over Newman Creek; and some houses, an access road
bridge and the water supply intake on Harvey Creek were damaged.
There was also evidence of local flooding of a small creek draining
a similar, very steep, west facing slope on Bowen Island about
10 km (6 mi) to the west of Lions Bay.

Very rough estimates from high water marks indicated
a peak discharge of about 115 m^3s^{-1} (4000 cusec) on Harvey Creek
and flows of about the same size (100 m^3s^{-1}) on Newman and
Strachan No. 2 Creeks. However, there was no evidence of
unusually high flows in Lone Tree Creek (between Harvey and
Newman Creeks) nor in the creeks north of Harvey Creek nor
south of Strachan Creek.

For comparison, the discharge with a 50 year return
period has been estimated at 11 $m^3s^{-1} km^{-2}$ (1000 cusec mi^{-2}) for
Mosquito Creek, a gauged creek with a steep watershed in North
Vancouver about 25 km (15 mi) away, which has been subject to
heavy flooding from time to time. Applying this rate to Harvey
Creek gives a peak flow of 80 m^3s^{-1} (2800 cusec), considerably
smaller than the estimated 115 m^3s^{-1}, indicating that the flood on
Harvey Creek was unusually high. The rates per unit area of the
much smaller Newman and Strachan Creeks were of course very
much greater.

APPARENT BEHAVIOR OF THE CREEKS

An inspection of the creek beds close to the road after
the floods showed that temporary dams had formed at, and been
washed away from several locations on Newman and Strachan
Creeks. One of these was due to a slide into the creek bed but the
others occurred at local changes in grade in the streambed. There
were reports of at least one similar dam in the steep upper reaches
of Harvey Creek, but no evidence of damming in the lower reaches,
where the slope is much less than that of the other two creeks.

225

The process which occurred is believed to be similar to that which can be observed when water is discharged at constant rate into the sloping face of a sand pile. The water begins to form a channel by eroding the sand but the sand gets deposited at the first local flattening of the slope and forms a "dam." Water builds up behind the dam and eventually the dam washes out. The mixture of sand and water surges down the slope, picking up more sand as it moves, until the mixture reaches another local flattening of the slope whereupon the water drains out of the mixture and the sand "jells," forming another dam. Water leaks through the little dams and "reservoirs" can be building up at several locations, then releasing as the dams break, then rapidly eroding more sand, jelling at changes in slope, etc. The whole process gives an impression of intermittent surges with much higher peak rates of discharge than the steady inflow.

The evidence from Newman Creek in particular tended to support the above theory. A profile of Newman Creek is shown in Figure 2. A temporary dam 6 to 9 m (20 to 30 ft) high had obviously formed at a flat spot just below a waterfall about 120 m (400 ft) upstream from the road. The creek bed between the dam and the road was scoured deeply and a large quantity of material had been deposited where the slope flattened at the road bridge -- deposited both under and on top of the bridge.

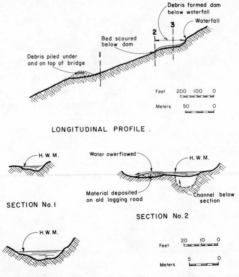

LONGITUDINAL PROFILE.

SECTION No. 1

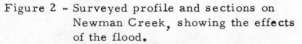

SECTION No. 2

SECTION No. 3

Figure 2 - Surveyed profile and sections on Newman Creek, showing the effects of the flood.

226

There was no evidence of appreciable debris movement or flood damage downstream of the road bridge. One could imagine the temporary dam building up during the flood; then giving way and releasing a surge of water and debris which made the stream bed almost "come alive;" and finally jelling at the bridge section.

At Strachan No. 2 Creek conditions were similar and there was evidence of at least two dams having built up and washed away, including one due to a slide into the creek. However, there the debris did not stop at the bridge but swept on down to the sea taking both the road and railway bridges with it. In the two years following the flood there was little further movement of debris in the creek beds, giving further evidence of the unusual nature of the floods.

SUMMARY

In September 1969 local floods of unusual magnitude occurred on three very steep creeks in the Lions Bay area. From inspection of the creeks afterwards it was deduced that temporary damming had occurred on at least two of the creeks. It is believed that the destruction caused by the flood may have been largely due to the surges resulting from washout of the temporary dams.

Chapter 5-5

RIVER REGIME STUDIES IN WESTERN ALBERTA.

Rolf Kellerhals

In the settled southern and central plains regions of
Alberta surface runoff is generally less than 2 in (5 cm), and over
major parts of South Saskatchewan, less than 0.5 in (1.25 cm)
(Neill et al, 1970). This small runoff is also unevenly distributed,
being associated mainly with a brief snowmelt period and infrequent
convective storms during the summer. Runoff rates rise gradually
through the foothills towards the Rockies, reaching over 40 in
(100 cm) near the continental divide. As a consequence all three
Prairie Provinces are heavily dependent on runoff from the Rockies
for their water supplies.

To improve water availability for irrigation, power
production, municipal use and sewage dilution during winter, when
natural flows are low, many small and intermediate storage schemes
have been built to date, and a relatively large scheme (Big Horn
Development on the North Saskatchewan River near Nordegg, mainly
for power production and winter-flow augmentation at Edmonton) is
presently under construction. If present trends of population growth
and economic development should persist, more and larger schemes
could be needed, including possibly southward diversions from less
intensely utilized rivers such as the North Saskatchewan and the
Athabasca.

During the sixties it became increasingly more apparent
that reservoir siltation was endangering some of the existing water
management schemes[1] and that the proposed larger schemes might
initiate river regime changes with far reaching and potentially
dangerous consequences (see Slaymaker, this volume). In order
to provide a sound basis for the study and prediction of these rather
poorly understood phenomena, extensive river regime studies were
initiated by four cooperating agencies, the Water Resources
Division of the Alberta Department of Environment, the Bridge

---

[1]At the Bassano diversion dam on the Bow River, the
sediment deposits have recently reached the irrigation intake. The
Glenbow Reservoir on the Elbow River at Calgary has lost some of
its usefulness for flood protection as a result of sedimentation
(Hillingshead, 1969).

Branch of the Alberta Department of Highways and Transport, the Highway and River Engineering Division of the Research Council of Alberta and the Department of Civil Engineering, University of Alberta. This report contains brief outlines of the major projects undertaken to date with references to resulting reports and publications.

OUTLINE OF PROJECTS

Survey of 108 River Reaches at Hydrometric Sites

In order to develop relations between discharge regime, hydraulic geometry and geologic and geomorphic setting of river reaches, 108 river surveys have been completed. The sites are somewhat unevenly distributed across Alberta with few sites north of latitude 56° and a heavy concentration of sites in the mountains and foothills of south-western Alberta.

The reaches are generally 1 to 2 meander bends long with the hydrometric site near the centre. The field surveys consists of a slope measurement, 5 to 10 cross-sections, bed material samples, a thalweg sounding, photographs, and descriptive coding sheets dealing with such parameters as bank materials and geomorphic aspects. The final data consist of mean geometric parameters (and their variance) for flows of several durations and return periods, mean bed material sizes, and extensive numeric codes dealing with engineering works affecting flow, quality of survey, general terrain, climate, valley and channel character- istics. The flow data are obtained by applying the stage-discharge relation of the hydrometric section to all other surveyed sections. Bankfull discharges have also been determined, using two or three different criteria (low level bench, vegetation trim line, and valley flat level). The final data have been placed on magnetic tape and can be made available, together with documented FORTRAN pro- grams for print-out, corrections, and analysis (Arora, et al, 1972). As a valuable by-product these surveys have produced an efficient methodology for river surveys (Bray, 1971; Neill, 1967) consisting of coding forms, computer programs, and instructions for their use. The wide variety of methods used for obtaining bed material samples necessitated an investigation of gravel sampling methods which led to the development of criteria for equivalence (Kellerhals and Bray, 1971a; 1971b).

Regime Analysis of Alberta Rivers

A generalized analysis of the above data has been completed recently (Bray, 1971). A major part of the study is devoted to comparisons between the Alberta data and river regime

investigations based on rivers in Alberta and British Columbia
(Blench and Qureshi, 1964; Kellerhals, 1967; Galay, 1970; Neill,
1967; 1968). Whenever possible, the data have been stratified
according to parameters such as bed material size, geomorphic
aspects (e.g. "entrenched" vs. "not obviously aggrading or
degrading"), bank materials, or depth to bedrock. The concept of
dominant discharge is also investigated in detail indicating that no
one particular discharge (e.g. 5 year flood) is consistently most
closely related to all geometric parameters, but the 2-year flood
and the bankfull discharge for the valley flat level are shown to be
superior to most others for general use.

Sediment Transport Studies

In cooperation with the Water Survey of Canada sediment
transport in steep gravel-bed rivers has become the subject of an
extensive investigation. Steep and highly active gravel rivers are
typical for south-western Alberta and their sediment load needs to
be estimated if reservoirs are to be properly designed. The normal
suspended load measuring techniques of the Water Survey are
inadequate because a significant portion of the total load consists of
bed-load. Published bed-load formulae gave inconsistent and
widely divergent results. To develop better procedures, bed-load
was measured at two sites (Figure 1), the Elbow River at Bragg

Figure 1 - Location Map

Creek and the North Saskatchewan River at Nordegg. The Bragg Creek results are readily available (Hollingshead, 1971). Various measuring techniques were tried, samples, tracer methods and excavation of a sediment trap downstream of a bedrock sill. One of the most significant results is, that bed-load transport computations can be vastly improved if the hydraulic conditions for initiation of movement and the width of the active strip are determined in the field. This can be done readily with a hydrophone, a directional crystal transducer built into a heavy sinker and operated from a bridge or cableway.

Hydrophone observations have now been made at over 50 sites (Yaremko, 1971) and it is planned to determine the conditions for beginning of gravel-bed movement at most suitable hydrometric sites in Alberta.

River Profiles

Since reliable river profiles are one of the basic requirements for water resources studies, an effort has been made to produce accurate profiles for the major rivers of Alberta. At present, profiles are available for all the rivers shown on Figure 1, with the exception of the Smoky River. The profiles show the water surface for the long-term mean flow, bed-rock levels and type where available (mainly at bridge and dam sites), and the top of the valley level on the left and on the right.

Illustrated Report on "Hydraulic and Geomorphic Characteristics of Rivers in Alberta"

In order to make the extensive data collections discussed above more readily available, a summary report is presently being prepared and should be ready by fall of 1972. It will contain the final results of the 108 river surveys (in abbreviated form and with words substituted for the numeric codes) and the river profiles. Twenty of the 108 surveyed reaches are illustrated on annotated air photo triplets. All the more common river types found in Alberta are being shown. An excellent example of a braided river is illustrated in Figure 2; the sharp discontinuity in the centre of the reach unfortunately has influenced the reliability of the survey. The surveyed cross-sections are indicated on the photo, the hydrometric site being marked "G." Lower case letters refer to the annotations, reproduced here in Table I.

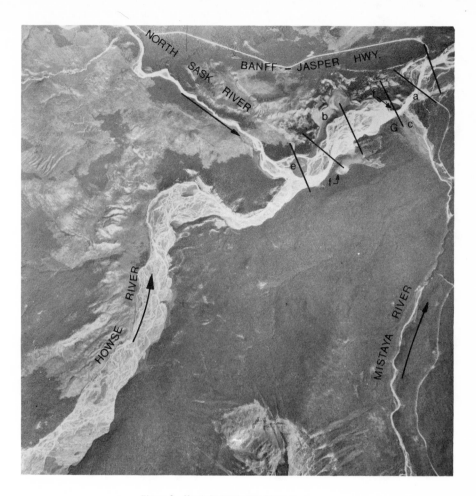

Figure 2 - North Saskatchewan River at
Saskatchewan Crossing.

TABLE I: Annotations to Figure 2

Location of Gauge: Sec. 35, Tp. 34, Rg. 20, W. 5.
51° 58' 00" / 116° 43' 30"

Photography: Government of Alberta Photographs. 1" = 3,333', August 11,
1952. Q = 5,120 c.f.s.

Terrain Surrounding Valley: Junction of 3 wide, mountainous valleys, with
extensive glacio-fluvial deposits. Remnants of an end moraine and ice
stagnation topography are visible near the study reach.

Channel Pattern: *Howse River and North Saskatchewan River downstream of
Section U2:* sinuous and braided, except for a short reach at the bridge,
where the Mistaya fan confines the North Saskatchewan River to one
channel. *Mistaya River and upper Saskatchewan River:* sinuous and
entrenched.

Channel Environment: The braided channel sections are frequently confined by
hummocky till, terraces, and alluvial fans. The valley flat consists of
isolated areas of overbank deposition (active flood plain). Remnants of a
low terrace appear like high islands in the braided channel.

Channel Processes: The channels of the braided section are highly unstable and
the braided pattern also indicates a high bedload transport rate. The width
of the braided section is gradually being enlarged through erosion of the
confining deposits.

Prominent Features: (a) Naturally confined channel segment. (This gives an
indication of the width to which the channel can be confined
artificially by coarse gravel.)
(b) Valley flat.
(c) Alluvial fan of the Mistaya River.
(d) Deep, narrow canyon in bedrock.
(e) Remnant of low terrace level.
(f) Kettle in ice-stagnation topography.

Chapter 5-6
SEDIMENT YIELD AND SEDIMENT CONTROL IN THE CANADIAN CORDILLERA.
H. Olav Slaymaker

It has been pointed out elsewhere (e.g. Pretious, 1969) that Canada has lagged behind the United States in sedimentation studies, one of the ostensible reasons being that "most Canadian rivers are not alluvial" (Stichling and Smith, 1968, p. 1) and that "many Canadian rivers carry comparatively light loads of sediment" (Pretious, 1969, p. 2). In the provinces of Alberta and British Columbia and in the Yukon Territory, by contrast with the rest of Canada, the sediment problem is extremely important. The reasons for its importance in the Cordilleran region can be attributed to (a) the extensive distribution of unconsolidated Pleistocene sediment; (b) receding glaciers and icefields are actively making entrained sediment available to fluvial systems and (c) the available relief and basin hypsometry encourages active slope and river processes (Corbel, 1959). Official figures on costs incurred by the sediment problem are not readily available. In the United States, a recent estimate of $175,000,000 per year was thought to be conservative (Task Committee on Preparation of Sedimentation Manual, 1969a).

From the Annual Report of the Water Resources Service of British Columbia for 1968, the Rivers and Harbours Branch of the Department of Public Works, Canada and the Sediment Survey of Canada, Table I and Figure 1 have been compiled to give a qualitative estimate of the sediment problem in British Columbia in the one year, 1968. The information should be interpreted with caution as there has been no weighting of the relative significance of each problem. What is most interesting is that, apart from the concentration of remedial activity in the Lower Mainland and Vancouver Island, there are some evident hazard zones in southern B. C. They are particularly well marked in those steep-sided glaciated valleys of the west coast which happen to be populated such as the Kitimat, Bella Coola and Squamish Valleys. Also, the Lillooet Valley and the Rocky Mountain Trench are areas of recurring sediment problems. It is regrettable that, to the present, so little contribution has been made by physical geographers towards the interpretation of this problem. An understanding of factors influencing sediment sources, modes of

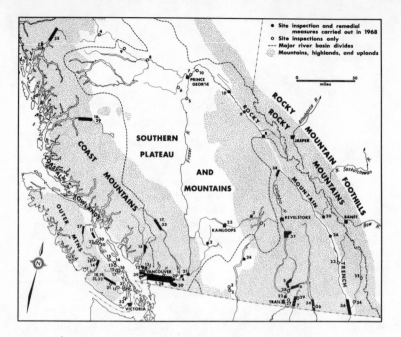

5-6   Figure 1 – The sediment problem in southern
B.C. (1968)

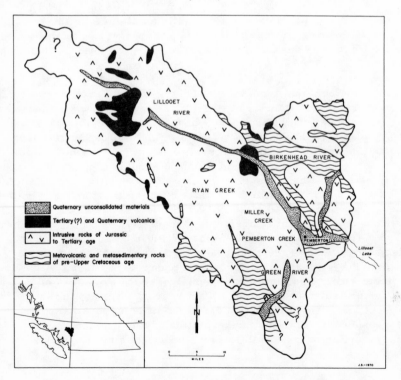

Figure 2 – Sediment sources in Lillooet River
basin (modified after W.H. Mathews)

TABLE 1 — The sediment problem in British Columbia 1968

A. Action (Indicated by solid symbol)

Floodplain deposition and bank erosion (1-20)	Drainage ditch and irrigation sediment (21-25)	Urban, road, mining logging effects (26, 27)	Surveys (28-35)	Reservoir sediment (36-38)	Channel dredging (39)
1. Lower Fraser Valley	21. Coquihalla River	26. Edgewater	28. Lower Fraser Valley	36. U. Kootenay	39. Lower Fraser Valley
2. Guichon Creek	22. Blueberry Creek	27. Buttle Lake	29. Bella Coola	37. U. Arrow	
3. Ross Creek	23. Brocklehurst		30. Chilliwack	38. Mica	
4. Lorenzetta Creek	24. Canyon Creek		31. Somenos Creek		
5. Slocan River	25. Chilliwack River		32. Cowichan River		
6. Kootenay River			33. Lillooet River		
7. Salmo River			34. Kootenay River		
8. Valemount			35. Kitimat River		
9. McBride					
10. Dome Creek					
11. Tsolum River					
12. N. & W. Vancouver					
13. Hastings Creek					
14. Port Alberni					
15. Lower Squamish Valley					
16. Bella Coola River					
17. Lillooet River					
18. Cassidy					
19. Langford Lake					
20. Bugaboo River					

B. Site Inspection (Indicated by open circle)

Floodplain deposition and bank erosion (1-22)		Urban, road, mining and logging effects (23-32)
1. Eagle River	12. Chase River	23. Canal Flats
2. Keremeos Creek	13. Lantzville	24. Elko
3. Olalla Creek	14. Nanoose Bay	25. Sparwood
4. Houston	15. Qualicum Bay	26. Creston
5. Hixon	16. Nanaimo	27. Fruitvale
6. Mud River	17. Harewood	28. Thrums
7. Prince George	18. Sproat Lake	29. Salmo
8. Vanderhoof	19. Duncan	30. Courtenay
9. Burns Lake	20. Comox	31. Duncan
10. Giscome	21. Mesachie Lake	32. Malahat
11. Cowichan River	22. Courtenay	

sediment distribution, sediment yield rates* and sediment control
measures available seems to be a prerequisite and three of these
areas are geomorphological in nature. Only sediment yield rates
in so far as they influence sediment control measures will be
considered here. The discussion is organized around three spatial
scales, arbitrarily designated: (a) larger than 25,000 km^2; (b)
250-25,000 km^2; (c) smaller than 250 km^2.

THE CANADIAN CORDILLERAN REGION (> 25,000 km^2)

Sediment Yield

The region covers $1.6 \times 10^6 km^2$. In Characterising
sediment yield rates for such a large region, ranging from the 49th
parallel to north of the Arctic Circle, there are inevitable problems
of lack of homogeneous data coverage. However, in so far as the
suspended load of the major rivers of the Peace, Fraser, Columbia,
South Saskatchewan and Mackenzie are a reliable index, it appears
that there is comparatively small variability in sediment yield data
at this scale (Table II).

It is recognized that bed load movement accounts for a
comparatively small proportion of the total clastic load (c. 10% of
the suspended load for the Fraser River: Pretious, 1969) and the
dissolved load (chemicals and salts in solution), though extremely
important volumetrically, is excluded from the present discussion.
Table II, together with unpublished data for the Mackenzie River
basin, (P. Lewis, pers. comm.) of which 28% is in the Cordillera,
suggest that the mean denudation rate for the region varies from
0.05 to 0.22 mm yr^{-1}. The rates for the Peace River are probably
inflated by a factor of 2 because of the intensive land use between
the Rocky Mountain Foothills and Peace River. Even so, the mean
rates (0.05-0.12 mm yr^{-1}) are high by comparison with many other
temperate and subarctic environments; in general, only regions
with more extensive unconsolidated Pleistocene deposits, such as
the loess region of China, and those with more extensive glacierization and active regional uplift, such as the Karakoram Mountains
of West Pakistan (Hewitt, 1968) show values markedly greater than
these (Table III). The data for the Gota River basin in Sweden
(Sundborg, 1964) appear to be representative of sediment yields in

---

*The term sediment yield rate is used rather loosely as
the amount of clastic sediment passing a given river cross-section
over a given time period. The units are expressed as either weight
per unit area of basin per unit time period or as a length dimension
per unit time period, assuming a mean specific gravity of sediments
of 2.71 (Mathews and Shepard, 1962).

TABLE II — Sediment load of rivers in the Canadian Cordillera

	Drainage Area (km²)	Sediment yield (10³ tons yr⁻¹)		Bed Load (10³ tons yr⁻¹)	Specific Denudation (mm yr⁻¹)
		Suspended Load (10³ tons yr⁻¹)			
A. Major river basins (> 25,000 km²)					
Fraser River above Hope (1966-67)	216,000	24,000		2,400*	0.08
Fraser River at delta (1929-59)	235,000		25,000		0.07
Peace River at Peace River (1966-67)	185,000	55,000		5,500*	0.22
Peace River at Peace Point (1967)	300,000	90,000		9,000*	0.20
Columbia River at Revelstoke (1967)	26,000	4,400		440*	0.12
S. Saskatchewan River at Highway 41 (1967)	66,000	8,200		820*	0.09
B. Intermediate river basins (250 - 25,000 km²)					
Lillooet River at Lillooet Lake (1858-1945)	3,800		1,450		0.25
Harrison River at Harrison Hot Springs (1966-67)	8,350	67		—	0.005
Chilliwack River at Vedder Crossing (1966-67)	1,250	92		—	0.05
Stave River at Stave Falls (1966-67)	1,100	16		—	0.01
Oldman River near Brocket (1966-67)	4,400	805			0.12
Elbow River at Reservoir (36 years)	1,220		113		0.06
Elbow River at Bragg Creek (1967-69)	780		58		0.05
C. Small watersheds (< 250 km²)					
Sentinel Creek (1967)	6	8			0.88
Marmot Creek (1964-67)	9	0.058			0.004
Athabasca River (1958)	28	0.8			0.019
Garibaldi Lake (1952-54)	38	9.3			0.161
Site studies					
Wernecke Mountains talus (Yukon Territory)	1.8				0.04
Ogilvie Mountain talus (Yukon Territory)	11.2				0.009
Nigel Creek overland flow (Alberta)	0.0004				0.005
Coast Mountains landslides (B.C.) A.	2.5				0.06
Coast Mountains (clear logged) B.	2.5				0.175

*Estimated as 10% of suspended load.

239

the humid temperate environment, namely 1 to 2 orders of magnitude lower than those of the Canadian Cordillera.

The regional implications of comparatively high sediment yield are apparent both in the severity of the sediment control problem (Figure 1) and in the distinctive landform assemblages commonly consisting of: (a) slope failure forms associated with rapid mass wasting: (b) braided streams associated with rapid sediment transport: (c) large, rapidly growing deltas and (d) steep river basins with relief-length ratios of 0.005 or greater (e.g. Fahnestock, 1969; Williams and Rust, 1969).

Sediment Control

The major sediment control considerations at this large regional scale are (a) harbour and channel dredging and (b) floodplain deposition and bank erosion in the major river basins.

(a) Fraser River dredging. Dredging of the Fraser River channels from New Westminster to the river mouth, a distance of 35 km (22 mi), removes an average of about 2 million tons of sediment per year (Pretious, 1958). Some of this is deposited on the river banks and some is barged to sea and dumped in the Straits of Georgia. Development of industrial plants along the banks of the Fraser River in this same reach since 1880 has induced shoaling so that extensive river training works have also been necessary (Pretious, 1960).

(b) Peace and Fraser Rivers: floodplain deposition and bank erosion. Investigations into the Peace River valley between the W. A. C. Bennett Dam in B. C. and the Alberta border suggest that slumping of the banks in unconsolidated material and the clearing of land for agricultural purposes in the Interior Plains region are the major factors leading to increased suspended sediment transport by the Peace River downstream (Kellerhals, pers. comm.). Floodplain deposition is not a serious problem in that the valley floor is relatively undeveloped. Farm buildings are generally located on terraces well above the floodplain, and the only floodplain hazard is presented to the P. G. E. and Alaska Highway bridges, both near Taylor. Similarly, the northern rivers of British Columbia, such as the Liard (Doughty-Davies, 1962), present hazards to the Alaska Highway bridges.

In the Fraser River valley also, major inputs of sediment can be ascribed to bank erosion (Kidd, 1953). Glacial drift, extensive aggradational sand and gravel and lake silt banks border the river from Lillooet to the river mouth, and provide a ready sediment source. Land clearing on the other hand is not thought to be a major influence on sediment yield rates. Floodplain deposition below Hope is a serious hazard, as illustrated by the effects of the 1948 flood. Therefore the dyking system established in 1948 to protect communities such as Chilliwack is being actively maintained. River bank protection projects were carried out in 12 districts in the Lower Mainland in 1968, for which the total expenditure was $220,000. The Governments of Canada and British Columbia intend to spend $36,000,000 over 10 years (1968-78) on upgrading dykes, building new dykes and providing river bank protection in the Lower Fraser. Although this is seen as primarily a flood problem, it is clear that the sediment problem forms a major component of it.

INTERMEDIATE SCALE RIVER BASINS
(250-25,000 km^2)

Sediment Yield

At this spatial scale, the variability of sediment yield data becomes strikingly apparent. Whereas at the regional scale, values of suspended sediment transport per unit area of drainage basin were very similar, Table II shows, for example, that Lillooet River at Lillooet Lake has a sediment yield 50 times as great as that of the Harrison River below Harrison Lake, and 5 times as great as that of the Elbow River at Bragg Creek in Alberta (Hollingshead, 1971). In the first case, the high sediment yield rates are influenced by the degree of glacierization (more than 10% of the basin area); the extensive unconsolidated Pleistocene sediment (5% of the basin area); the presence of erodible recent volcanic rocks (6% of the basin area) (Figure 2) and relief-length ratio of 0.03. The Harrison River is influenced by the presence of two large lakes upstream which act as settling basins for most of the sediment. This factor also accounts for the comparatively low rates recorded for the Stave River. The Elbow River basin has no glacierized area, no erodible volcanics and a more restricted distribution of unconsolidated sediments than the Lillooet River basin, and these appear to be the parameters which distinguish the two basins. The unglacierized Austrian basin quoted by Lanser (1958), the partly glacierized subarctic Rapaälven basin (Sundborg, 1964) and the Lillooet River basin during a period of accelerated erosion are included in Table III for comparative purposes.

Sediment Control

The major sediment control considerations at this spatial scale are primarily in the area of river regulation. It is true that local river dredging problems, as at the Squamish River delta, are significant but problems of river regulation such as those of the

Squamish, Lillooet, Bella Coola, and Kemano Rivers, are most typical.

The principles of stream channel improvement and stabilisation can be summarized as follows: (a) to understand the fluvial morphology and present depositional environment (Lane, 1955; Flaxman, 1965); (b) to maintain stream thalweg gradient; (c) to strengthen banks to resist flowing water; (d) to create bank roughness to reduce velocity (e.g. vegetative control of stream bank erosion, Parsons, 1965); (e) to divert flow from erodible banks; (f) to convey the water and sediment with maximum efficiency.

(a) Lillooet River regulation. During the 1946-1951 period, 38 km (24 mi) of dykes, 14 km (9 mi) of river cutoffs, 27 km (17 mi) of ditches and 14 km (9 mi) of service and construction roads were completed in the valley of the Lillooet River. At the same time the high water level of Lillooet Lake was lowered by 2-1/2 m (8 ft). The net effect of the river training and the lake level lowering was an increase in the average gradient of the Lillooet River over a 50 km (32 mi) reach from 0.0008 to 0.001, thereby violating one of the principles outlined above. Since 1953, the river has degraded considerably so that farmers now need to irrigate land that formerly had a high water table. At the same time, total sediment discharged into Lillooet Lake has increased, and the flood hazard appears to have increased significantly, partly as a result of the aggradation of the lower reaches of the floodplain. What was originally conceived as a flooding problem is now seen to be primarily a sediment problem.

(b) Squamish River. Regulation of the Squamish River has been necessary because of the building of industrial plant and development of the built-up area of Squamish, almost all on the floodplain of the Squamish River. The distinctive "sediment" carried by the river is composed of logs from the Pacific Ranges of the Coast Mountains which go to form log jams and are instrumental in gravel bar growth and changes in channel form and location. In 1968, $250,000 was spent on bank protection and dyke construction on the lower Mamquam and Squamish Rivers.

(c) Kemano River. The Kemano River, an actively braiding river, illustrates a third problem in river regulation. No part of the floodplain is here safe for settlement or communications, and the response has been to construct all roads and settlement, at greater initial cost, well above the floodplain.

242

SMALL WATERSHED AND SITE STUDIES
(< 250 km^2)

Sediment Yield

      Studies conducted at the small watershed scale can lead
to greater physical understanding of the factors which are
responsible for local variations in sediment yield. They are
commonly sufficiently small that the confounding influence of man
and changing land use practices can be eliminated or introduced
under control. In addition, site studies can be helpful in isolating
specific sediment source areas even though it is difficult to predict
the integrated effect of many such source areas in a small watershed. The small watershed data quoted in Tables II and III show
even greater variability than those at the intermediate scale. They
indicate that a small urban construction area in Maryland (Wolman
and Schick, 1967) has the highest sediment yield, and Marmot
Creek in the Canadian Rocky Mountains has the lowest sediment
yield. The low sediment yield from the latter steep basin derives
from the stabilisation of the lower slopes by forest growth as only
a part of the basin is above tree line. By contrast, the Sentinel
Creek, Athabasca River and Garibaldi Lake are entirely within the
alpine zone.

      The results of site studies quoted in this volume are
particularly interesting, especially those of O'Loughlin in relation
to landslide activity in the Coast Mountains. He shows that even at
undisturbed sites, the denudation rate attributable to landslides can
be as much as 0.06 mm yr^{-1}. Where clear logging is carried out,
a rate nearly 3 times as great can be anticipated. This provides
Canadian Cordilleran confirmation of Fredriksen's (1970)
observation in Oregon.

      Gray quotes rates for talus cone development in the
Yukon Territory and Dingwall quotes rates of sediment moved by
overland flow in the alpine zone in the Alberta Rocky Mountains.
These are significant but highly localized processes whose contribution when integrated over a whole basin becomes extemely small.
Gardner (1969) has investigated rock fall frequency on slopes of
differing aspect in the Lake Louise area. Bank erosion has not
been measured here, but it has been measured in unconsolidated
Pleistocene deposits in Britain (Kirkby, 1967; Slaymaker, 1972)
and proved to be the dominant sediment producing process in that
area.

Sediment Control

      The major sediment control considerations at this small

watershed and site scale are radically different from those at the
larger spatial scales. The basic principles of sediment control in
small watersheds have been laid out by the Task Committee on
Preparation of a Sedimentation Manual (1969b) and they include:
(a) to use each acre within its capacity for sustained use without
deterioration of the soil resource; (b) to develop a combination of
land use practices and structural measures to control water movement and (c) to preserve a balance between the needs of (i) each
acre, (ii) the small watershed, and (iii) the larger river basin
to which it is tributary. Land use influences on sediment yield,
and the interaction of physiography and land use are of prime
significance at this scale (Slaymaker and Jeffrey, 1969).

(a) Forest Harvesting

　　　Logging roads, landings and skid trails associated with
forest harvesting accentuate sediment problems. In the Lillooet
River basin between 1945 and 1969, 20,000 acres were logged. The
average acreage logged per year since 1967 has been 12 times as
great as in the late 1940's. Jeffrey (1968) noted most severe sediment problems in the west Kootenay region where a combination of
steep topography, high precipitation intensity and erodible soils
create high hazard conditions. Goodell (in this volume) describes
the procedure for testing the influence of logging on water quality
by use of the paired experimental watershed approach. Table I
indicates a number of investigations into this problem in the
Kootenays and on Vancouver Island in 1968.

(b) Agricultural Land Clearance

　　　Forest clearance for agricultural land use is increasing
rapidly in the Canadian Cordillera. Savini and Kammerer (1961)
have reported increases in sediment yield of one to two orders of
magnitude in the eastern U. S. A. resulting from this land use
change. In the B. C. Coast Mountain valleys the particularly severe
problem is the instability of channel banks resulting from vegetation
clearance, of which the Lions Bay flood of 1969 is a good example,
(Russell, in this volume).

(c) Road Construction and Mining Developments

　　　O'Bryan and McAvoy (1966) have reported 2-3 orders of
magnitude sediment yield increase in areas stripped for road construction and Jeffrey (1968) has noted extensive influence of highway
construction in the Columbia Mountains of B. C. Table I indicates
potential problems at Buttle Lake and in the Elk Valley from
mining development.

CONCLUSION

Problems of sediment yield and control in the Canadian Cordillera are of theoretical as well as practical interest. The simplistic models of Langbein and Schumm (1958) and Fournier (1960) in which sediment yield is seen as a function of climatic variables are inadequate for this region; likewise the interpretation of all sediment yield rates as artifically accelerated by man and his varied land use practices (Douglas, 1967) does not explain the variability of sediment yield at a variety of spatial scales. The important factors in this discussion have been spatial scale, Pleistocene legacy both of sediment and ice, the steep topography and a variety of land use practices. These important factors influencing sediment yield lead to spatially variable sediment control needs in the Canadian Cordillera. The prime categories of sediment control measures presently employed are channel, drainage ditch and irrigation canal improvements; there is as yet little evidence of controlled land use practices such that sustained yield and minimum soil disturbance principles can be applied towards sound land and river management.

TABLE III: Comparative specific denudation rates (excluding dissolved load)

		Drainage Area (km^2)	Specific Denudation ($mm. \ yr^{-1}$)
A.	**Major river basins (>25,000 km^2)**		
	Ching River (China)	57,000	4.9
	Upper Indus River (W. Pakistan)	190,000	1.1
	Mackenzie River	1,850,000	0.02
	Gota River (Sweden)	50,000	0.002
B.	**Intermediate river basins (250 - 25,000 km^2)**		
	Lillooet River at Lillooet Lake (1946 - 69)	3,800	1.0
	Rapaalven (Sweden) (12% glaciers)	680	0.1
	Lech R. et Steeg (Austria) (no glaciers)	250	0.02
C.	**Small watersheds (< 250 km^2)**		
	Construction site (Johns Hopkins University)	0.001	36.3
	Venter Ache R. at Vent (Austria) (45.7% glaciers)	165	1.0
	H.J. Andrews Experimental Forest (Oregon)		
	Patch cut with roads (1960 - 68)	0.15	2.0
	Chamberlain (Alaska)	3.7	0.25
	H.J. Andrews Experimental Forest (Oregon)		
	Control watershed (1960 - 68)	0.09	0.02

BIBLIOGRAPHY

Aitken, J. D. and R. G. Greggs, 1967. Upper Cambrian
formations, southern Rocky Mountains of Alberta, an
interim report. Geol. Surv. Can. Paper 66-49, 91 pp.

Anderson, E. A. and D. M. Rockwood, 1970. Runoff synthesis
for rain-on-snow basin. Proc. 38th West. Snow. Conf.,
pp. 82-90.

Anderson, H. W., R. M. Rice, and A. J. West, 1958. Snow in
forest openings and forest stands. Proc. Soc. Amer.
Foresters, 58th Annual Meeting, pp. 46-50.

Anderton, L. J., 1970. Quaternary stratigraphy and geomorphology
of the lower Thompson Valley, British Columbia. Unpubl.
M. A. Thesis, Univ. of British Columbia.

Armstrong, J. E., 1956. Surficial geology of Vancouver Area,
British Columbia. Geol. Surv. Can. Paper 55-40, 16 pp.

_____, 1957. Surficial geology of New Westminster Area,
British Columbia. Geol. Surv. Can. Paper 57-5, 25 pp.

_____, 1960a. Surficial geology of Sumas map-area, British
Columbia. Geol. Surv. Can. Paper 59-9, 27 pp.

_____, 1960b. Surficial geology of the Chilliwack (west half)
map-area, British Columbia. Geol. Surv. Can. Prelim.
Map 53-1959.

_____, 1965. Geology, Vancouver North, B. C. Geol. Surv.
Can. Map 1152A.

_____, 1968. Field trip to illustrate geology of Coast Mountains,
North Vancouver, B. C. Guidebook for Geological Field Trips
in Southwestern B. C. Dept. of Geol., Univ. of British
Columbia, Rept. 6, pp. 25-38.

Armstrong, J. E. and W. L. Brown, 1954. Late Wisconsin marine
drift and associated sediments of the Lower Fraser Valley,
British Columbia, Canada. Bull. Geol. Soc. Amer., 65,
pp. 349-364.

247

Armstrong, J. E., D. R. Crandell, D. J. Easterbrook and J. B. Noble, 1965. Late Pleistocene stratigraphy and chronology in southwestern British Columbia and northwestern Washington. Bull. Geol. Soc. Amer., 76, pp. 321-330.

Armstrong, J. E. and R. J. Fulton, 1965. In INQUA 7th Congress, 1965. Guidebook for Field Conference J, Pacific Northwest, 108 pp.

Arora, V. K., R. Kellerhals, and D. I. Bray, 1972. A Program Package for Storage and Analysis of River Data. Rept., Highway and River Eng. Div., Res. Council of Alberta.

Atwood, W. W., 1945. The Rocky Mountains. Vanguard Press, 324 pp.

Baumgartner, H., 1965. Energetic bases for differential vaporization from forest and agricultural lands. Proc. Int. Symp. on Forest Hydrol., Pergamon Press, pp. 381-389.

Beaty, C. B., 1963. Origin of alluvial fans, White Mountains, California and Nevada. Ann. Assoc. Amer. Geog. 53, pp. 516-535.

_____, 1970. Age and estimated rate of accumulation of an alluvial fan, White Mountains, California, U.S.A. Amer. J. Sc. 268, pp. 50-77.

Bell, H. S., 1942. Density currents as agents for transporting sediments. J. Geol. 50, pp. 512-547.

Beloussov, V. V., 1962. Basic Problems of Geotectonics. Trans. P. T. Broneev, McGraw-Hill, 816 pp.

Beschel, R. E., 1961. Dating rock surfaces by lichen growth and its application to glaciology and physiography (lichenometry). In Geology of the Arctic, Vol. 2, (G. O. Raasch, ed.), Univ. of Toronto Press, p. 1044-1062.

Betson, R. P. and J. B. Marius, 1969. Source areas of storm runoff. Water Resources Res. 5 (3), pp. 574-582.

Bishop, D. M. and M. E. Stevens, 1964. Landslides in logged areas in Southeast Alaska. U. S. Forest Serv., Res. Paper NOR-1, 57 pp.

Blackwelder, E., 1928. Mudflow as a geological agent in semi-arid mountains. Bull. Geol. Soc. Amer. 39, pp. 465-483.

Blissenback, E., 1954. Geology of alluvial fans in semi-arid regions. Bull. Geol. Soc. Amer. 65, pp. 175-190.

Blench, T., 1969. Mobile Bed Fluviology. Univ. of Alberta Press, 168 pp.

Blench, T. and M. A. Qureshi, 1964. Practical regime analysis of river slopes. Proc. Amer. Soc. Civ. Eng. 90, pp. 81-98.

Bluck, J., 1964. Sedimentology of an alluvial fan in southern Nevada. J. Sed. Petrol. 34, pp. 395-400.

Boesch, H. H., 1946. Die formen des hochgebirges. Die Alpen 22, pp. 293-299.

Boulton, G. S., 1968. Flow tills and related deposits on some Vestspitsbergen glaciers. J. Glaciol. 7, pp. 391-412.

Boydell, A. N., 1970. Relationship of late-Wisconsin Rocky Mountain and Laurentide Ice in the vicinity of Sundre, Alberta. Unpubl. M. Sc. Thesis, Univ. of Calgary.

Bray, D. I., 1971. Generalized Regime Type Analysis of Alberta Rivers. Unpubl. Ph. D. Thesis, Univ. of Alberta.

Brink, V. C., 1959. A directional change in the Sub-Alpine Forest-Health ecotone in Garibaldi Park, B. C. Ecology 40, pp. 10-15.

British Columbia Department of Lands, Forests and Water Resources, 1969. Water Resources Service Annual Report for 1968, 110 pp.

Broscoe, A. J. and S. Thompson, 1969. Observations on an Alpine mudflow, Steele Creek, Yukon. Can. J. Earth. Sc. 6, pp. 219-229.

Brundall, J. A., 1966. Recent debris flows and related gullies in the Cass Basin. Unpubl. M. A. Thesis, Univ. of Canterbury.

Brunger, A. G., 1966. Drummond, Hector and Peyto Glaciers: Their Wastage and Deposits. Unpubl. M. Sc. Thesis, Univ. of Calgary.

Brunger, A. G., J. G. Nelson and I. Y. Ashwell, 1967. Recession of the Hector and Peyto Glaciers: Further studies in the

Drummond Glacier, Red Deer River Valley, Alberta. Can. Geog., 11, pp. 35-48.

Bruch, L. M., 1961. Drainage basins, channels, and flow characteristics of selected streams in central Pennsylvania. U. S. Geol. Survey Prof. Paper 282-F, pp. 145-181.

Bryan, R. B., 1969. The relative erodibility of soils developed in the Peak District of Derbyshire. Geog. Ann., 51A (3), pp. 145-159.

Bull, W. B., 1964. Geomorphology of segmented alluvial fans in Western Fresno County, California. U. S. Geol. Survey, Prof. Paper 352-E, pp. 89-129.

Cailleux, A., 1963. Initiation a l'Etude des Sables et des Galets. Centre de Documentation Universitaire I, 151 pp.

Caine, T. N., 1969. A model for alpine talus slope development by slush avalanching. J. Geol. 77, pp. 92-101.

Cairness, E. E., 1927. Observations on Lillooet Valley, B. C. Can. Mining J. 48, pp. 140-144 and 162-166.

Campbell, I. A., 1970. Erosion rates in the Steveville Badlands, Alberta. Can. Geog. 14, pp. 202-216.

Campbell, P. I., I. A. Reid and J. Shastal, 1969. Glacier Survey in Alberta, Canada. Dept. Energy, Mines and Resources, Inland Waters Branch, Rept. 4, 16 pp.

Canada Department of Energy, Mines and Resources, Inland Waters Branch, 1969. Glacier Surveys in British Columbia, Rept. 5, 18 pp.

Canada Department of Energy, Mines and Resources, Inland Waters Branch, 1965-67. Sediment Data for Canadian Rivers. Ottawa: Queen's Printer.

Carson, M. A., 1971. An application of the concept of threshold slopes to the Laramic Mountains, Wyoming. Inst. Brit. Geog. Spec. Pub. 3, pp. 30-48.

Christiansen, E. A., 1965. Ice frontal positions in Saskatchewan. Sask. Res. Council (Geol. Div.) Map No. 2.

Church, M. A., 1970. Baffin Island Sandar, a Study of Arctic

Fluvial Environments. Unpubl. Ph. D. Thesis, Univ. of British Columbia.

Church, M. A. and R. Kellerhals, 1970. Stream Gauging in Isolated Areas Using Portable Equipment. Canada Dept. of Energy, Mines and Resources, Inland Waters Branch Tech. Bull. No. 25, 90 pp.

Churcher, C. S., 1968. Pleistocene ungulates from the Bow River Gravels at Cochrane, Alberta. Can. J. Earth Sc., 5, pp. 1467-1488.

Clauzon, G. and J. Vaudour, 1969. Observations sur les effets de la pluie en Provence. Zeit. fur Geomorph., 13, pp. 390-405.

Coates, D. R., 1969. Hydraulic geometry in a glaciated region. Paper presented at Amer. Geophys. Union Ann. Meeting, April 24, 1969, Washington, D. C., 19 pp.

Coleman, A. P., 1912. The Canadian Rockies. Frowde, 383 pp.

Collier, E. P., 1957. Glacier variation and trends in runoff in the Canadian Cordillera. Int. Assoc. Sc. Hydrol., Spec. Publ. 46, pp. 344-357.

Conway, W. M., 1893. Exploration in the Mustagh Mountains. Geog. J. 2, pp. 289-299.

Corbel, J., 1959. Vitesse de l'erosion. Zeit. fur Geomorph. 3, pp. 1-28.

Coutts, J. R. H., M. F. Kandil, J. L. Nowland and J. Tinsley, 1968. The use of radioactive ^{59}Fe for tracing soil particle movement. I Field studies of splash erosion. J. Soil Sc. 19, pp. 311-324.

Croft, A. R., 1962. Some sedimentation phenomena along the Wasatch Mountain front. J. Geophys. Res., 67, pp. 1511-1524.

Croft, A. R. and J. A. Adams, 1950. Landslides and sedimentation in the North Fork of the Ogden River, May, 1949. U. S. D. A. Forest Serv. Res. Paper NOR-1, 18 pp.

Curry, R. R., 1966. Observation of alpine mudflows in the Tenmile Range, Central Colorado. Bull. Geol. Soc. Amer. 77, pp. 771-776.

Daly, R. A., 1905. Summit levels among alpine mountains. J. Geol., 13, p. 105.

_____, 1912. Geology of the North American Cordillera at the 49th Parallel. Geol. Surv. Can. Mem. 38, 857 pp.

Davies, K. F., 1964. Survey of Glaciers on the Eastern Slope of the Rocky Mountains in the Banff and Jasper National Parks, Canada. Department of Northern Affairs and National Resources, Water Resources Branch.

Davis, W. M., 1923. The cycle of erosion and the summit level of the Alps. J. Geol. 31, pp. 1-41.

Day, T. J., 1970. The Channel Geometry of Mountain Streams. Unpubl. M. A. Thesis, Univ. of British Columbia.

Denny, C. S. and H. Drewes, 1965. Geology of the Ash Meadows Quadrangle, Nevada. U. S. Geol. Survey Bull. 1181-L, pp. 22-27.

Dollfus, O., 1960. Etude d'un bassin torrentiel dans la vallee du Rimac, Andes Centrales Peruviennes. Rev. Geomorph. Dyn. 11, pp. 159-163.

Douglas, D., 1914. Journal Kept by David Douglas during his Travels in North America, 1823-27. Antiquarian Press, 364 pp.

Douglas, I., 1967. Man, vegetation and the sediment yields of rivers. Nature, 215, pp. 925-928.

Doughty-Davies, J. H., 1962. Liard River Basin Sedimentation Study. British Columbia Water Resources Report 1010, Water Rights Branch, B. C. Department of Lands, Forests and Water Resources.

Dyrness, C. T., 1967. Mass soil movements in the H. J. Andrews Experimental Forest. U. S. Forest Serv. Res. Pap. PNW-42, 12 pp.

Easterbrook, D. J., 1964. Void ratios and bulk densities as a means of identifying Pleistocene tills. Bull. Geol. Soc. Amer. 75, pp. 745-750.

_____, 1969. Pleistocene chronology of the Puget Lowland and San Juan Islands, Washington. Bull. Geol. Soc. Amer.

80, pp. 2273-2286.

Ekern, P. C., 1964. Direct interception of cloud water on Lanaihale, Hawaii. Proc. Soil Sc. Soc. Amer., 28, pp. 419-421.

Ellison, W. D., 1945. Some effects of raindrops and surface flow on soil erosion and infiltration. Trans. Amer. Geophys. Union, 26, pp. 415-429.

Elrick, D. E. and J. H. M. Aalders, 1968. Mechanics of the movement of moisture and chemical substance in soils. Proc. Hydrol. Symp. No. 6: Soil Moisture, Nat. Res. Council of Can., pp. 51-79.

Embleton, C. and C. A. M. King, 1968. Glacial and Periglacial Geomorphology. Arnold, 608 pp.

Emmett, W. W., 1970. The hydraulics of overland flow on hillslopes. U. S. Geol. Survey Prof. Paper, 662-A, 68 pp.

Endo, T. and T. Tsurata, 1969. The effect of tree roots on the shearing strength of soil. Annual Report, Forest Exp. Stn., Hokkaido. pp. 167-182.

Fahnestock, R. K., 1969. Morphology of the Slims River. Amer. Geog. Soc. Icefield Ranges Res. Proj. Sc., Results, I, pp. 161-171.

Falconer, G., W. E. S. Henoch and G. M. Ostrem, 1966. A glacier map of southern British Columbia and Alberta. Geog. Bull. 8, pp. 108-112.

Field, W. O., 1949. Glacier observations in the Canadian Rockies 1948. Can. Alpine J. 32, pp. 99-114.

Field, W. O. and C. J. Heusser, 1954. Glacial study in the Canadian Rockies. Can. Alpine J. 37, pp. 128-140.

Flaccus, E., 1959. Landslides and their Revegetation in the White Mountains of New Hampshire. Unpubl. Ph. D. Thesis, Duke University.

Flaxman, E. M., 1965. Some aspects of fluvial morphology influencing investigations of channel stability. U. S. Dept. of Agriculture, Misc. Pub. 970, pp. 136-143.

Flint, R. F., 1957. Glacial and Pleistocene Geology. Wiley, 553 pp.

Folk, R. L., 1965. Petrology of Sedimentary Rocks. Univ. Texas Manual, Hemphills, Austin, 154 pp.

Fournier, F., 1960. Climat et Erosion. Presses Universitaires de Paris.

Fredriksen, R. L., 1970. Erosion and sedimentation following road construction and timber harvest. U. S. D. A. Forest Serv. Res. Paper PNW-104, 15 pp.

Frye, J. C., H. B. Willman and R. F. Black, 1965. Outline of glacial geology of Illinois and Wisconsin. In The Quaternary of the United States (H. E. Wright and O. G. Frey, eds.), Princeton Univ. Press, 11. 43-61.

Fryxell, F. M. and L. Horberg, 1943. Alpine mud flows in Grand Teton National Park Wyoming. Bull. Geol. Soc. Amer., 54, pp. 457-472.

Fulton, R. J., 1965. Silt deposition in late-glacial lakes of southern British Columbia. Amer. J. Sc. 263, pp. 553-570.

_____, 1969. Glacial lake history, southern Interior Plateau, British Columbia. Geol. Surv. Can. Paper 69-37.

Fulton, R. J. and M. J. L. T. Pullen, 1969. Sedimentation in Upper Arrow Lake, British Columbia. Can. J. Earth Sc. 6, pp. 785-791.

Gaiser, R. N., 1952. Root channels and roots in forest soils. Proc. Soil Sc. Soc. Amer. 16, pp. 62-65.

Galay, V. J., 1970. Some Hydraulic Characteristics of Coarse-bed Rivers. Unpubl. Ph. D. Thesis, Univ. of Alberta.

Gann, E. E., 1969. Flood height frequency relations for the plains area in Missouri. U. S. Geol. Survey Prof. Paper, No. 600-D, 2 pp.

Gardner, J., 1967. Notes on avalanches, icefalls and rockfalls in the Lake Louise district, July and August 1966. Can. Alpine J. 50, pp. 90-95.

_____, 1968a. Debris Slope Form and Processes in the Lake

Louise District: A High Mountain Area. Unpubl. Ph. D. Thesis, McGill University.

_____, 1968b. Mountain temperatures. Can. Alpine J. 51, pp. 224-228.

_____, 1969a. Snow patches: their influence on mountain wall temperatures and the geomorphic implications. Geog. Ann. 51A, pp. 114-120.

_____, 1969b. Observations of surficial talus movement. Zeit. fur Geomorph. 13, pp. 317-323.

_____, 1970a. Geomorphic significance of avalanches in the Lake Louise Area, Alberta, Canada. Arctic and Alpine Res. 2, pp. 135-144.

_____, 1970b. Rockfall: a geomorphic process in high mountain terrain, Albertan Geog. 6, pp. 15-21.

_____, 1970c. A note on the supply of material to debris slopes. Can. Geog. 14, pp. 369-372.

Garner, J., 1968. Mountain temperatures. Can. Alpine J. 51, pp. 224-228.

Gartska, W. U., L. D. Love, B. C. Goodell and F. A. Bertle, 1958. Factors Affecting Snowmelt and Streamflow. U. S. Gov. Print. Office, 189 pp.

Gerlach, T., 1967. Hillslope trough for measuring sediment movement. Rev. Geomorph. Dyn., 17, p. 173.

Gilleran, D. J., 1968. Rapid Calibration of Coastal Streams to Detect Effects of Road Building. Unpubl. M. Sc. Thesis, Oregon State University.

Goldthwaite, R. P., A. Dreimanis, J. L. Forsyth, P. F. Karrow, and G. W. White, 1965. Pleistocene deposits of the Erie Lake. In The Quaternary of the United States (H. E. Wright and D. G. Frey, eds.), Princeton Univ. Press, pp. 85-97.

Gray, D. H., 1969. Effects of Forest Cutting on the Stability of Natural Slopes. Univ. of Michigan, Dept. of Civil Engineering Pub., 67 pp.

Gray, J. T., 1971. Processes and Rates of Development of talus

Slopes and Protalus Rock Glaciers in the Ogilvie and
Wernecke Mountains, Yukon Territory. Unpubl. Ph. D.
Thesis, McGill University.

Groom, G. E., 1959. Niche glaciers in Bünsow-land,
Vestspitzbergen. J. Glaciol. 3, pp. 369-376.

Hack, J. T. and J. C. Goodlett, 1960. Geomorphology and forest
ecology of a mountain region in the central Appalachians.
U. S. Geol. Survey Prof. Paper 347, 66 pp.

Hallin, W. E., 1967. Soil moisture and temperature trends in
cutover and adjacent old growth Douglas Fir timber. U. S.
D. A. Forest Serv. Res. Note PNW-56, 11 pp.

Harper, W. C., 1969. Changes in Storm Hydrographs Due to
Clearcut Logging. Unpubl. M. Sc. Thesis, Oregon State
Univ., 116 pp.

Harris, S. A., 1971. Preliminary observations on downslope
movement of soil during the fall at Kananaskis, Alberta.
Proc. Can. Assoc. Geog., Waterloo, pp. 199-206.

_____, 1972. Some types of instrumentation effective in
studies of soil creep near Calgary, Alberta. Can. Geog.
(In Press)

Harris, S. A. and E. Pip, 1972. Mollusca as a means of
determining late and post-glacial climatic history in Alberta.
Can. J. Zoology. (In Press)

Hartshorn, H. J., 1958. Flow till in S. E. Massachusetts.
Bull. Geol. Soc. Amer. 69, pp. 477-482.

Haupt, H. F., 1967. Infiltration, overland flow and soil
movement on frozen and snow-covered plots. Water
Resources, Res., 3 (1), pp. 145-161.

Hector, J., 1861. On the geology of the country between Lake
Superior and the Pacific Ocean and between the 48th and
54th parallels of latitude. Quart. J. Geol. Soc. London, 17,
pp. 388-455.

Henoch, W. E. S., 1971. Estimate of glaciers secular (1948-1966)
volumetric change and its contribution to the discharge in the
Upper North Saskatchewan River Basin. J. Hydrol. 12,
pp. 145-160.

Heusser, C. J., 1956. Postglacial environments in the Canadian Rocky Mountains. Ecological Monographs 26, pp. 263-302.

Hewitt, K., 1968. The freeze-thaw environment of the Karakoram Himalaya. Can. Geog., 12, pp. 85-98.

_____, 1967. Studies in the Geomorphology of the Mountain Regions of the Upper Indus Basin. Unpubl. Ph. D. Thesis, Kings College, Univ. of London, 2 vols.

Hewlett, J. D., 1961. Soil moisture as a source of base flow from steep mountain watersheds. U. S. Forest Serv., S. E. Forest and Range Expt. Stn. Paper 132, 11 pp.

Hewlett, J. D. and A. R. Hibbert, 1967. Factors affecting the response of small watersheds to precipitation in humid areas. Proc. Int. Symp. on Forest Hydrol, Pergamon Press, Toronto, pp. 275-290.

Hibbert, A. R., 1965. Forest treatment effects on water yield. Proc. Int. Symp. on Forest Hydrol., Pergamon Press, pp. 527-543.

Hills, R. C., 1970. The determination of the infiltration capacity of field soils using the cylinder infiltrometer. Brit. Geomorph. Res. Group, Tech. Bull., 3, 25 pp.

Hobbs, H. W., 1910. The cycle of mountain glaciation. Geog. J. 36, pp. 146-163.

Hollingshead, A. B., 1968. Measurements of the Bed-load Discharge of the Elbow River. Unpubl. M. Sc. Thesis, Univ. of Alberta.

_____, 1969. Sedimentation study, Glenmore Reservoir. Research Council of Alberta.

_____, 1971. Sediment transport measurements in gravel river. Proc. Amer. Soc. Civ. Eng. J. Hydraul. Div. 97, pp. 1817-1834.

Hoppe, G. and S. R. Ekman, 1964. A note on the alluvial fans of Ladtjovarre, Swedish Lapland. Geog. Ann. 46, pp. 338-342.

Horberg, L., 1952. Pleistocene drift sheets in the Lethbridge region, Alberta, Canada. J. Geol. 60, pp. 303-330.

Horberg, L., 1954. Rocky Mountain and Continental Pleistocene deposits in the Waterton region, Alberta, Canada. Bull. Geol. Soc. Amer. 65, pp. 1093-1150.

Horton, J.R. and R.H. Hawkins, 1965. Flow path of rain from the soil surface to the water table. Soil Sci. 100, pp. 377-383.

Houbolt, J.J.H.C. and J.B.M. Jonker, 1968. Recent sediments in the eastern part of the Lake of Geneva (Lac Léman). Geol. Mijnbow 47, pp. 131-148.

Hsieh, F.S., 1970. Storm runoff response from road building and logging on small watersheds in the Oregon Coast Range. Unpubl. M. Sc. Thesis, Oregon State University.

Hubley, R.C., 1956. Glaciers in the Washington Cascade and Olympic Mountains; their present activity and its relation to local climatic trends. J. Glaciol. 2, pp. 699-674.

Hursh, C.R., 1944. Chairman's report to subcommittee on sub-surface flow. Trans. Amer. Geophys. Union Pt. 5, pp. 743-746.

Ichikawa, M., 1958. On the debris supply from mountain slopes and its relation to river bed deposition. Science Reports, Tokyo Geog. Inst. Section C. 6, No. 49, 29 pp.

Il'In, N.I., 1970. Anomalies in water filtration through peat soils. Soviet Soil Sci. 4, pp. 508.

International Association of Scientific Hydrology 1966. International Symposium on Scientific Aspects of Snow and Ice Avalanches. Spec. Pub. 69, 421 pp.

Jackli, H., 1957. Gegenwartsgeologie des bundnerischen Rheingebietes-ein beitrag zur exogenen dynamik alpiner gebirgslandschaften. Beitrage zur Geologia der Schweiz, Geotech. Ser., Leiferung 36.

Jackson, R.J., 1966. Slips in relation to rainfall and soil characteristics. J. Hydrol. (NZ), 5, pp. 45-53.

Jahn, A., 1960. Some remarks on evolution of slopes on Spitsbergen. Zeit. für Géomorph., Supp. Bd., I, pp. 49-58.

Jeffrey, W.W., 1968a. Watershed management problems in British Columbia: a first appraisal. Water Resources Bull. 4, pp. 58-70.

Jennings, A.H., 1951. The glacial geomorphology of the Sunwapta Pass Area, Jasper National Park. Unpubl. M. Sc. Thesis, Univ. of Iowa.

Judd, H.E. and D.F. Peterson, 1969. Roughness of large bed element streams. Paper presented at Hydraul. Div., Amer. Soc. Civ. Eng., Annual Conf., Logan, Utah.

Karrasch, H., 1970. Das phenoma der klimabedingten reliefa-symmetrie in Mitteleuropa. Göttinger Geog. Abh. Hft 56, 299 pp.

Kellerhals, R., 1967. Stable channels with gravel-paved beds. Proc. Amer. Soc. Civ. Eng., J. Waterways and Harb. Div. 93, pp. 63-84.

_____, 1969. Runoff concentration in steep channel networks. Unpubl. Ph. D. Thesis, Univ. of British Columbia.

_____, 1970. Runoff routing through steep natural channels. Proc. Amer. Soc. Civ. Eng. J. Hydraul. Div. 96, pp. 2201-2217.

Kellerhals, R. and D.I. Bray, 1971a. Comments on 'An improved method for size distribution of stream bed gravel' by L.B. Leopold. Water Resources Res. 7, pp. 1045-1047.

_____, 1971b. Sampling procedures for coarse fluvial sediments. Proc. Amer. Soc. Civ. Eng. 97, pp. 1165-1180.

Kidd, G.J.A., 1953. Fraser River suspended sediment survey: Interim Report 1947-52. British Columbia Water Resources Report 322, Water Rights Branch, B.C. Department of Lands, Forests and Water Resources.

King, L., 1967. The Morphology of the Earth. (2nd Edn.) Hafner Co., 726 pp.

Kirkby, M.J., 1963. A study of rates of erosion and mass movement on slopes with special reference to Galloway. Unpubl. Ph. D. Thesis, Univ. of Cambridge.

_____, 1967. Measurement and theory of soil creep, J. Geol., 75, pp. 359-378.

Kittredge, J., 1948. Forest Influences. McGraw-Hill, 394 pp.

Lane, E.W., 1955. Design of stable channels. Trans. Amer. Soc. Civ. Eng. 120, pp. 1234-1279.

Langbein, W.B., 1964. Geometry of river channels. <u>Proc.</u>
<u>Amer. Soc. Civ. Eng., J. Hydraul. Div.</u>, 90, pp. 301-312.

Langbein, W.B. and S.A. Schumm, 1958. Yield of sediment
in relation to mean annual precipitation. <u>Trans. Amer.</u>
<u>Geophys. Union.</u> 39, pp. 1076-1084.

Langbein, W.B. and L.B. Leopold, 1964. Quasi-equilibrium
states in channel morphology. <u>Amer. Sci.</u>, 262, pp. 782-794.

Lanser, O., 1958. Reflexions sur les debits solides en suspension des cours d'eau glaciaires. <u>Bull. Int. Assoc. Sci.</u>
<u>Hydrol.</u> 4, pp. 37-43.

Lee, R., 1967. The hydrologic importance of transpiration
control by stomata. <u>Water Resources Res.</u> 3, pp. 737-752.

Leopold, L.B., 1953. Downstream changes of velocity in rivers.
<u>Amer. J. Sci.</u>, 251, pp. 606-624.

Leopold, L.B. and T. Maddock, 1953. The hydraulic geometry
of stream channels and some physiographic implications.
<u>U.S. Geol. Survey Prof. Paper</u> 252, 57 pp.

Leopold, L.B. and J.P. Miller, 1956. Ephemeral streams -
hydraulic factors and their relation to the drainage net.
<u>U.S. Geol. Survey Prof. Paper</u> 282-A, 32 pp.

Leopold, L.B. and W.B. Langbein, 1962. The concept of
entropy in landscape evolution. <u>U.S. Geol. Survey Prof.</u>
<u>Paper</u> 500-A.

Leopold, L.B., M.G. Wolman and J.P. Miller, 1964. <u>Fluvial</u>
<u>Processes in Geomorphology</u>, Freeman and Co., 522 pp.

Leopold, L.B., W.W. Emmett and R.M. Myrick, 1966.
Channel and hillslope processes in a semi-arid area, New
Mexico. <u>U.S. Geol. Survey Prof. Paper</u>, 352-G, pp. 192-253.

Leopold, L.B. and H.E. Skibitzke, 1967. Observations on
unmeasured rivers. <u>Geog. Ann.</u> 49A, pp. 247-255.

Liakopoulos, A.C., 1965. Darcy's coefficient of permeability
as symmetric tensor of second rank. <u>Bull. Int. Assoc. Sci.</u>
<u>Hydrol.</u> 10, pp. 41-48.

Lichti-Federovich, S., 1971. The pollen stratigraphy of a dated section of late-Pleistocene lake sediment from central Alberta. Can. J. Earth Sci., 7, pp. 938-945.

Lighthill, M.J. and B.G. Whitham, 1955. On kinematic waves: I. Flood movement in long rivers. Proc. Royal Soc. London, 229, pp. 281-316.

Löken, O.H. (ed.), 1969. North Saskatchewan Headwaters. Inland Waters Branch, Glaciology Subdiv., 52 pp. (restricted circulation).

Loup, J. and C. Lovie, 1967. Sur la frèquence des avalanches en Haute Tarentaise. Rev. Geog. Alpine. 55, pp. 587-604.

Luckman, B.H., 1970. The nature and variability of size sorting on talus slopes. Proc. Can. Assoc. Geog. Winnipeg, pp. 213-220

_____, 1971. The role of snow avalanches in the evolution of alpine talus slopes. Inst. Brit. Geog. Spec. Pub. 3, pp. 93-110.

Lustig, L.K., 1965. Clastic sedimentation in Deep Springs Valley. U.S. Geol. Survey Prof. Paper. 352-F, 192 pp.

Mackay, J.R. and W.H. Mathews, 1967. Observations on pressures exerted by creeping snow, Mount Seymour, B.C. Proc. Int. Conf. Low Temp. Sci., 1, pp. 1185-1197.

Markgren, M., 1964. Geomorphological studies in Fennoscandia II, Chute slopes. B. Systematic studies. Lund Studies in Geography, Ser. A, No. 28, 147 pp.

Matthes, F.E., 1938. Avalanche sculpture in the Sierra Nevada of California. Union Int. Geol. et Geophys, Bull. 23.

Mathews, W.H., 1944. Glacial lakes and ice retreat in south central British Columbia. Trans. Royal Soc. Can. 38 (4), pp. 39-57.

_____, 1950. Historic and prehistoric fluctuations of alpine glaciers in the Mount Garibaldi map-area; southwestern British Columbia. J. Geol. 59, pp. 357-380.

_____, 1952a. Mount Garibaldi, a supraglacial Pleistocene volcano in southwestern British Columbia. Amer. J. Sci., 250. pp. 81-103.

Mathews, W.H., 1952b. Ice dammed lavas from Clinker
Mountain, southwestern British Columbia. Amer. J. Sci.
250, pp. 553-565.

_____, 1956. Physical limnology and sedimentation
in a glacial lake. Bull. Geol. Soc. Amer. 67, pp. 537-552.

_____, 1958. Geology of the Mount Garibaldi map-
area, southwestern British Columbia, Canada. Part II:
Geomorphology and Quaternary volcanic rocks. Bull. Geol.
Soc. Amer. 69, pp. 179-193.

_____, 1964. Sediment transport from the Athabasca
Glacier, Alberta. Int. Assoc. Sci. Hydrol., Spec. Pub.
65, pp. 155-165.

_____, 1968. Geomorphology, southwestern British
Columbia. In "Guidebook for Geological Field Trips in
Southwestern British Columbia", Department of Geology,
University of British Columbia, Rept. 6, pp. 18-24.

Mathews, W.H. and F.P. Shepard, 1962. Sedimentation of the
Fraser River Delta, British Columbia. Amer. Assoc.
Petrol. Geol., 46, pp. 1416-1443.

Mathews, W.H. and J.R. Mackay, 1963. Snowcreep studies,
Mt. Seymour, B.C.: preliminary field investigation.
Geog. Bull. 20, pp. 58-75.

Mathews, W.H. and K.C. McTaggart, 1969. The Hope landslide,
B.C. Proc. Geol. Assoc. Can., 20, pp. 65-75.

Mathews, W.H., J.G. Fyles and H.W. Naismith, 1970. Post-
glacial crustal movements in southwestern British Columbia
and adjacent Washington state. Can. J. Earth Sci. 7,
pp. 690-702.

Mcdonald, B.C. and I. Banerjee, 1971. Sediments and bedforms
on a braided outwash plain. Can. J. Earth Sci. 8, pp. 1282-
1301.

McPherson, H.J., 1970. Landforms and glacial history of the
upper North Saskatchewan Valley, Alberta, Canada. Can.
Geog. 14, pp. 10-25.

_____, 1971. Downstream changes in sediment character
in a high energy mountain stream channel. Arctic and Alpine
Res. 3, pp. 65-79.

McPherson, H.J. and J. Gardner, 1969. The development of glacial landforms in the vicinity of the Saskatchewan Glacier. Can. Alpine J., 52, pp. 90-96.

Meier, M.F., 1960. Mode of flow of the Saskatchewan Glacier, Alberta, Canada. U.S. Geol. Survey Prof. Paper 351, 70 pp.

Meier, M.F. and A.S. Post, 1962. Recent variations in mass net budgets of glaciers in Western North America. Int. Assoc. Sci. Hydrol., Spec. Pub. 58, pp. 63-77.

Meiman, J.R., 1968. Snow accumulation related to elevation, aspect and forest canopy. In "Snow Hydrology Workshop Seminar", Can. Nat. Comm., Int. Hydrol. Decade, Fredericton, pp. 35-47.

Meyer, L.D. and E.J. Monke, 1965. Mechanics of soil erosion by rainfall and overland flow. Trans. Amer. Soc. Agric. Eng., 8, pp. 572-577.

Miller, J.P., 1958. High mountain streams: effect of geology on channel characteristics and bed material. New Mexico State Bur. Mines and Mineral Resources. Mem. No. 4, 53 pp.

Moldenhauer, W.C. and J. Koswara, 1968. Effects of initial clod size on characteristics of splash and wash erosion. Proc. Soil Sci. Soc. Amer., 32, pp. 875-878.

Morris, H.M., 1968. The hydraulics of energy dissipation in steep, rough channels. Virginia Polytechnic Institute, Res. Div., Bull. No. 19.

Morton, J.W., 1970. Capilano: The Story of a River. McClelland and Stewart Ltd., 184 pp.

Moss, I.H. and W.E. Bonini, 1961. Some evidence supporting a new interpretation of the Cody Terrace near Cody, Wyoming. Bull. Geol. Soc. Amer. 72, pp. 547-557.

Neave, K.G. and J.C. Savage, 1969. Seismic activity on the Athabasca Glacier. Trans. Amer. Geophys. Union 50, p 236.

Neill, C.R., 1967. Mean velocity criterion for scour of coarse uniform bed material. Proc., Int. Assoc. Hydraul. Res., Denver, Colórado.

Neill, C.R., 1968. A re-examination of the beginning of movement for coarse granular bed materials. Unpubl. Rep., Hydraulics Res. Station, Wallingford, U.K.

Neill, C.R. and V.J. Galay, 1967. Systematic evaluation of river regime. Proc. Amer. Soc. Civ. Eng. 93, pp. 25-53.

Neill, C.R., D.I. Bray, M.F. Schouten, and J.R. Card, 1970. Selected characteristics of streamflow in Alberta. Research Council of Alberta, Report 70-1, 55 pp.

Nelson, J.G., I.Y. Ashwell and A.G. Brunger, 1966. Recession of the Drummond Glacier, Alberta. Can. Geog. 10, pp. 71-81.

Nutter, W.L., 1969. Management implications of subsurface stormflow and the variable source concept. Proc. Soc. Amer. Foresters, 69th Annual Meeting.

Oberlander, T., 1965. The Zagros Streams. Syracuse Geogr. Ser. No. 1, Syracuse Univ., 168 pp.

O'Bryan, D. and R.L. McAvoy, 1966. Gunpowder Falls, Maryland. U.S. Geol. Survey Water Supply Paper 1815, 90 pp.

Ostrem, G., 1966a. The height of the glaciation limit in southern British Columbia and Alberta. Geog. Ann. 48A, pp. 126-138.

_____, 1966b. Mass balance studies in Western Canada. Geog. Bull., 8, pp. 81-107.

Ostrem, G., and K. Arnold, 1970. Ice-cored moraines in southern British Columbia and Alberta, Canada. Geog. Ann. 52A, pp. 120-128.

Parsons, D.A., 1965. Vegetative control of streambank erosion. U.S. Dept. of Agric. Misc. Pub. 1970, pp. 130-136.

Paterson, W.S.B., 1964. Variation in the velocity of the Athabasca Glacier with time. J. Glaciol., 5, pp. 277-285.

_____, 1970. The sliding velocity of the Athabasca Glacier. J. Glaciol., 9, pp. 55-63.

Patric, J.H., J.E. Douglas and J.D. Hewlett, 1965. Soil water absorption by mountain and piedmont forests. Proc. Soil Sci. Soc. Amer. 29, pp. 303-308.

Penck, A., 1919. Die Gipfelflur der Alpen. Sitzber. Preuss. Akad. Wiss.

Peterson, D.F. and P.K. Mohanty, 1960. Flume studies in steep rough channels. Proc. Amer. Soc. Civ. Eng., J. Hydraul. Div., 86, pp. 55-76.

Pheasant, D.R., 1968. The glacial geomorphology of the Ya-Ha Tinda area, Alberta. Unpubl. M. Sc. Thesis, University of Calgary.

Porter, S.C. and G.H. Denton, 1967. Chronology of Neo-glaciation in the North American Cordillera. Amer. Sci., 265, pp. 177-210.

Potter, N., 1968. Tree-ring dating of snow avalanche tracks and the geomorphic activity of avalanches, northern Absaroka Mountains, Wyoming. Geol. Soc. Amer. Spec. Paper 123, pp. 141-165.

Pretious, E.S., 1958. Estimate of quantity rate of bed-load transport in the Fraser River estuary. University of British Columbia Fraser River Model. Report 229.

_____, 1960. Historical review of river training and its effects in the New Westminster area, Fraser River, B.C. University of British Columbia. Fraser River Model Report 233.

_____, 1969. The sediment load of the lower Fraser River, B.C. Department of Civil Engineering Report, University of British Columbia, 27 pp.

Price, R.A. and E.W. Mountjoy, 1970. Geologic structure of of the Canadian Rocky Mountains between Bow and Athabasca Rivers - a progress report. Can. Geol. Assoc. Spec. Paper 6, pp. 7-25.

Rainwater, F.H. and H.P. Guy, 1961. Some observations on the hydrochemistry and sedimentation of the Chamberlain Glacier area, Alaska. U.S. Geol. Survey Prof. Paper 414-C, 14 pp.

Randle, K., G.C. Goles and L.R. Kittleman, 1971. Geochemical and petrological characterization of ash samples from Cascade Range volcanoes. Quaternary Res., I, pp. 261-282.

Rapp, A., 1958. Om bergras och laviner i Alperna. Ymer 78, pp. 112-131.

_____, 1959. Avalanche boulder tongues in Lappland. Geog. Ann., 41, pp. 34-48.

_____, 1960a. Recent development of mountain slopes in Karkevagge and surroundings, northern Scandinavia. Geog. Ann., 42, pp. 65-200.

_____, 1960b. Talus slopes and mountain walls at Tempelfjorden, Spitsbergen. Norsk Polarinstitutt Skrifter. 119, 96 pp.

_____, 1963. The debris slides at Ulvadal, western Norway: an example of catastrophic slope processes in Scandinavia. Nachrichten Gottingen Gesellschaft der Wissenschaften. Math. phys. Klass No. 13, pp. 195-210.

Raymond, C.F., 1971. Flow in a transverse section of the Athabasca Glacier, Alberta, Canada. J. Glaciol., 10, pp. 55-84.

Reinelt, E.R., R. Kellerhals, M.A. Moldt, W.M. Schultz and W.E. Stevens, 1971. Proceedings of the Peace-Athabasca Delta Symposium, University of Alberta, 359 pp.

Richmond, G.M., 1965. Glaciation in the Rocky Mountains. In "The Quaternary of the United States", (H.E. Wright and O.G. Frey, eds.), Princeton Univ. Press, pp. 217-230.

_____, 1970. Comparison of the Quaternary stratigraphy of the Alps and Rocky Mountains. Quaternary Res., 1, pp. 3-28.

Rickmers, W.R., 1913. The Duab of Turkestan. Cambridge Univ. Press, 563 pp.

Riley, J.P., D.G. Chadwick and K.O. Eggleston, 1969. Snow-melt simulation. Proc. 37th. West. Snow Conf., pp. 44-48.

Roddick, J.A., 1965. Vancouver, Coquitlam and Pitt Lake map areas, B.C. Geol. Surv. Can., Memoir 335, 276 pp.

Roed, M.A., et al., 1967. The Athabasca Valley erratics train, Alberta, and Pleistocene ice movements across the Continental divide. Can. J. Earth Sci., 4, pp. 625-632.

_____, 1968. Surficial geology of the Edson-Hinton area, Alberta. Unpubl. Ph. D. Thesis, Univ. of Alberta.

Rothacher, J., 1970. Increases in water yield following clear-cut logging in the Pacific Northwest. Water Resources Res. 6, pp. 653-658.

_____, 1971. Regimes of streamflow and their modification by logging. Proc. Symp. on Forest Land Uses and Stream Environment, Oregon State Univ., pp. 40-50.

Russell, R.J., 1933. Alpine landforms of the western United States. Bull. Geol. Soc. Amer. 44, pp. 927-950.

Russell, S.O., 1970. Flood control in the Pemberton Valley. Unpubl. Class Project. Civil Engineering 598, Univ. of British Columbia.

Rutter, N.W., 1965. Surficial geology of the Banff area, Alberta. Unpubl. Ph.D. Thesis, Univ. of Alberta.

_____, 1966. Glacial history of the Bow Valley, Banff area, Alberta. Can. Alpine J. 49, pp. 157-173.

Rutter, A.J., 1968. Water consumption by forests. In "Water Deficits and Plant Growth, Plant Water Consumption and Response" (T.T. Koslowski, ed.), Academic Press, pp. 23-84.

Rutter, N.W., 1972. Geomorphology and multiple glaciation of the area of Banff, Alberta. Geol. Surv. Canada Bull. (In Press).

Ruxton, B.P., 1967. Slopewash under a mature primary rainforest in northern Papua. In "Landform Studies from Australia and New Guinea". (J.N. Jennings and J.A. Mabbutt, eds.) ANU Press, pp. 85-94.

Ryder, J.M., 1970. Alluvial fans of post-glacial environments within British Columbia. Unpubl. Ph. D. Thesis, Univ. of British Columbia.

Ryder, J.M., 1971a. The stratigraphy and morphology of paraglacial alluvial fans in south-central British Columbia. Can. J. Earth Sci. 8, pp. 279-298.

Samide, G., 1971. Sediment transport measurements. Unpubl. M. Sc. Thesis, Univ. of Alberta.

Savigear, R.A.G., 1956. Technique and terminology in the investigation of slope forms. Int. Geog. Union, Slopes Commission, Rio de Janeiro, pp. 66-75.

Savini, J. and J.C. Kammerer, 1961. Urban growth and water regimes. U.S. Geol. Survey Water Supply Paper 1591-A, 42 pp.

Schaerer, P.A., 1962. The avalanche hazard evaluation and prediction at Rogers Pass. Nat. Res. Council, Div. Bldg. Res., Ottawa. Technical Paper 142.

_____, 1970. Variation of ground snow loads in British Columbia. Proc. 38th West. Snow Conf., pp. 44-48.

Scheidegger, A.E., 1970. Theoretical Geomorphology. 2nd. Ed. Revised. Springer-Verlag, 435 pp.

Scheuerlein, Helmut, 1968. Der Rauhgerinneabflus. Technischen Hochschule Munchen, Oskar V. Miller Institut. Bericht. No. 14 Versuchsantalt für Wasserbau.

Schroeter, L., 1925. Taschenflora des Alpenwanderers. Revised Edn., Zurich.

Schumm, S.A., 1954. The relation of drainage basin relief to sediment loss. Int. Assoc. Sci. Hydrol., Spec. Pub. 36, pp. 216-219.

_____, 1963. The disparity between present rates of denudation and orogeny. U.S. Geol. Survey, Prof. Paper 454-H.

_____, 1964. Seasonal variations of erosion rates and processes on hillslopes in western Colorado. Zeit. für Geomorph. Supp. Bd. 5, pp. 215-238.

Seagel, G.C., 1971. The morphological and sediment characteristics of the Elbow River Basin. Unpubl. M. Sc. Thesis, Univ. of Alberta.

Sedgewick, K., 1965. Geomorphology and mass budget of the Peyto Glacier, Alberta. Unpubl. M. Sc. Thesis, McMaster University.

Seligman, G., 1936. Snow Structure and Ski Fields. Macmillan.

Sharp, R.P., 1942. Mudflow levees. J. Geomorph. 5, pp. 222-227.

Sharp, R.P. and L.N. Nobles, 1953. Mudflows of 1941 at Wrightwood, S. California. Bull. Geol. Soc. Amer. 64, pp. 547-560.

Sharpe, C.F.S., 1938. Landslides and Related Phenomena. Columbia University Press, 137 pp.

Sheng, T.C., 1966. Landslide classification and studies of Taiwan. Chinese-Amer. Joint Comm. on Rural Reconstruction; Forestry Series No. 10, 96 pp.

Sherzer, W.H., 1907. Glaciers of the Canadian Rockies and Selkirks. Smithsonian Contributions to Knowledge, 34 (1092), pp. 1-135.

Slaymaker, H.O., 1968. Patterns of subaerial erosion in instrumented catchments. Unpubl. Ph. D. Thesis, Univ. of Cambridge.

_____, 1972. Patterns of present subaerial erosion and landforms in mid-Wales. Trans. Inst. Brit. Geog., 55 (in press).

Slaymaker, H.O. and W.W. Jeffrey, 1969. Physiography-land use interactions in watershed management. In "Water Balance in North America", (A.H. Laycock, et al., eds.), pp. 170-181

Smith, W.O., C.P. Vetter and G.B. Cummings, et al. 1960. Comprehensive survey of sedimentation in Lake Mead, 1948-1949. U.S. Geol. Survey Prof. Paper 295, 254 pp.

Smith, D.D. and W.H. Wischmeier, 1962. Rainfall erosion. Advances in Agronomy, 14, pp. 109-148.

Sneed, E.D. and R.L. Folk, 1958. Pebbles in the lower Colorado River, Texas - a study in particle morphogenesis. J. Geol. 66, pp. 114-150.

Soons, J. M. and J. N. Rayner, 1968. Micro-climate and erosion processes in the Southern Alps, New Zealand. Geog. Ann. 50A, pp. 1-15 and 120-122.

Spreizer, H., 1960. Hangformung und asymmetrie der bergrücken in den Alpen und im Tarus. Zeit. für Géomorph. Contributions Int. à la Morph. des Versants., pp. 211-236.

Stalker, A. Mac S., 1956. The erratics train, foothills of Alberta. Geol. Surv. Can., Bull. 37, 28 pp.

_____ , 1963. Surficial geology of Blood Indian Reserve No. 148, Alberta. Geol. Surv. Can., Paper 63-25, 20 pp.

_____ , 1968. Geology of the terraces at Cochrane, Alberta. Can. J. Earth Sci., 5, pp. 1455-1466.

_____ , 1969. A probable late Pinedale terminal moraine in Castle River Valley, Alberta. Bull. Geol. Soc. Amer. 80, pp. 2115-2122.

Stene, L. P., 1966. Pleistocene valley terraces along the Athabasca River in the Hinton area. Unpubl. M. Sc. Thesis, University of Alberta.

Stichling, W. and T. F. Smith, 1968. Sediment Surveys in Canada. Canada Dept. Energy, Mines and Resources, Inland Water Branch. 17 pp.

Stiny, Josef, 1910. Die Muren. Innsbruck, Wagnerschen Universitats - Buchhandlung, 130 pp.

Stork, A., 1963. Plant immigration in front of retreating glaciers, with examples from the Kebnekajse area, northern Sweden. Geog. Ann. 45, pp. 1-22.

Strahler, A.N., 1956. Quantitative slope analysis. Bull. Geol. Soc. Amer., 67, pp. 571-596.

Sundborg, A., 1964. The importance of the sediment problem in the technical and economic development of river basins. Kungl. Vetenskapssamhällets i Uppsala Arbok. 8, pp. 33-52.

Suslov, S.P., 1956. Physical Geography of Asiatic Russia (2nd. Edn). Trans. by N.D. Gershevsky (J.E. Williams, ed.), Freeman and Co., 594 pp.

Sutton, C.W., 1933. Andean mud slide destroys lives and property. Eng. News-Record, 110, pp. 562-563.

Swanston, D.N., 1967. Geology and slope failure in the Maybeso Valley, Prince of Wales Island, Alaska. Unpubl. Ph. D. Thesis, Michigan State Univ.

_____, 1969. Mass wasting in coastal Alaska. U.S. D.A. Forest Serv. Res. Paper PNW-83, 15 pp.

_____, 1970. Mechanics of debris avalanching in shallow till soils of southeast Alaska. U.S.D.A. Forest Serv. Res. Paper PNW-103, 17 pp.

Task Committee on Preparation of Sedimentation Manual, 1969a. Sedimentation engineering. Chapter VI: Economic aspects of sedimentation. Proc. Amer. Soc. Civ. Eng., J. Hydraul. Div., 95, pp. 191-207.

_____, 1969b. Chapter V: Sediment control methods. Introduction and watershed area. Proc. Amer. Soc. Civ. Eng., J. Hydraul. Div., 95, pp. 649-675.

_____, 1970. Sediment sources and sediment yields. Proc. Amer. Soc. Civ. Eng., J. Hydraul. Div. 96, pp. 1283-1329.

Ter-Stepanian, G., 1963. On the long term stability of slopes. Norwegian Geotech. Instit. Pub. No. 52, pp. 1-15.

Terzaghi, K., 1950. Mechanism of landslides. In "Applications of Geology to Engineering Practice". Geol. Soc. Smer., Berkey Volume, pp. 83-123.

_____, 1956. Varieties of submarine slope failures. Harvard Univ. Soil Mechanics Series, 52, 41 pp.

Tharin, J.C., 1960. Glacial geology of the Calgary area, Alberta. Unpubl. Ph. D. Thesis, Univ. of Illinois.

Thom, H.C.S., 1966. Distribution of maximum annual water equivalent of snow on the ground. Monthly Weather Review, pp. 265-271.

Thompson, W.F., 1962. Cascade alp slopes and gipfelfluren as climageomorphic phenomenena. Erdkunde, 26, pp. 81-94.

271

Thorington, J.M., 1927. The Lyell and Freshfield Glaciers. Smithsonian Misc. Collections, 78 (6), pp. 1-8.

Thornes, J., 1971. State, environment and attribute in scree-slope studies. Inst. Brit. Geog. Spec. Pub. 3, pp. 49-63.

Tipper, H.W., 1971. Multiple glaciation in central British Columbia. Can. J. Earth Sci. 8, pp. 743-752.

Tsukamato, Y., 1961. An experiment on subsurface flow. Jap. For. Soc. J. 43, pp. 61-68.

Tricart, J., 1957. Une lave torrientelle dans les Alpes Autrichiennes. Rev. Geomorph. Dyn. 8, pp. 161-165.

Troll, C., 1943-1944. Strukturboden, solifluction und frostklima der erde. Geol. Rundschau, 34, pp. 545-694.

U.S. Army, 1956. Snow hydrology, Corps of Engineers, U.S. Army, Portland, 437 pp.

Varnes, D.J., 1958. Landslide types and processes. In "Landslides and Engineering Practice". National Res. Council Pub. 544, Highway Res. Board Spec. Rept. 29, pp. 20-47.

Vaux, W.S., 1909. Modern glaciers. Can. Alpine J. 2, pp. 56-78.

Veyret, P., 1959. L'eau, la neige, la glace, le gel et la structure dans l'evolution morphologique de la region Chamonix. Rev. Géog. Alpine. 47.

Vinogradov, Yu. B., 1969. Some aspects of the formation of mudflows and methods of computing them. Soviet Hydrol., 5, pp. 480-500.

Wagner, W.P., 1966. Correlation of Rocky Mountain and Laurentide Glacial Chronologies in southwest Alberta. Unpubl. Ph. D. Thesis, Univ. of Michigan.

Wahrhaftig, C., 1965. Stepped topography of the southern Sierra Nevada. Bull. Geol. Soc. Amer., 76, pp. 1165-1190.

Walker, M.J.C., 1971. Late-Wisconsin ice in the Morley Flats area of the Bow Valley and adjacent areas of the Kananaskis Valley. Unpubl. M. Sc. Thesis, Univ. of Calgary.

272

West, R., and A. Maki, 1961. An advancing glacier in Canada. Science, 133, p. 1361.

Wester, J., 1967. Pemberton Valley Dyking District drainage proposals. Water Resources Report 1440, Water Rights Branch, B.C. Department of Lands, Forests and Water Resources.

Westgate, J.A. and A. Dreimanis, 1967. Volcanic ash layers of recent age at Banff National Park, Alberta, Canada. Can. J. Earth Sci., 4, pp. 155-161.

Westgate, J.A., D.G.W. Smith and M. Tomlinson, 1970. Late Quaternary tephra layers in southwestern Canada; "Early Man and Environments in Northwestern North America". The Students Press, Calgary, pp. 13-34.

Weyman, D.R., 1970. Through flow on hillslopes and its relation to the stream hydrograph. Bull. Int. Assoc. Sci. Hydrol. 15, pp. 25-33.

Wheeler, A.O., 1931. Glacial change in the Canadian Cordillera. Can. Alpine J., 20, pp. 120-142.

_____, 1933. Records of glacial observations in the Canadian Cordillera. Can. Alpine J., 22, pp. 172-185.

White, S.E., 1968. Rockfall, alluvial and avalanche talus in the Colorado Front Range. Abstr. Geol. Soc. Amer. 1967, p. 237.

Whipkey, R.Z., 1969. Storm runoff from forested catchments by subsurface routes in floods and their computations. Int. Assoc. Sci. Hydrol. Spec. Pub. 85, pp. 773-779.

Wilcox, R.E. and H.A. Powers, 1964. Volcanic ash from Mount Mazama (Crater Lake) and from Glacier Peak. Science, 144, pp. 1334-1336.

Williams, P.F. and B.R. Rust, 1969. The sedimentology of a braided river. J. Sed. Petrol. 39, pp. 649-679.

Winder, C.G., 1965. Alluvial cone construction by alpine mudflow in a humid temperate region. Can. J. Earth Sci. 2, pp. 270-277.

Wolman, M.G., 1955. The natural channel of Brandywine Creek, Pennsylvania. U.S. Geol. Survey Prof. Paper 271, 56 pp.

Wolman, M.G. and J.P. Miller, 1960. Magnitude and frequency of forces in geomorphic processes. . Geol., 68, pp. 54-74.

Wolman, M.G. and A.P. Schick, 1967. Effects of construction of fluvial sediment, urban and suburan areas of Maryland. Water Resources Res. 3, pp. 451-464.

Yaremko, E., 1971. Summary report c. hydrophone measurements. Internal Technical Report, Alberta Dept. of the Environment, Water Resources Di

Young, A., 1960. Soil movement by denudational processes on slopes. Nature, 188, pp. 120-122.

Young, R.A. and R.F. Holt, 1968. Tracing soil movement with fluorescent glass particles. Proc. Soil Sci. Soc. Amer., 32, pp. 600-602.

Young, R.A. and C.K. Mutchler, 19. . Soil movement on irregular slopes. Water Resour es Res., 5, pp. 1084-1089.

Zaslavsky, D. and A.S. Rogowski, 1969. Hydrologic and morphologic implications of anisotropy and infiltration in soil profile development. Proc. Soil Sci. Soc. Amer. 33, pp. 594-599.

Zinke, P., 1965. Influence of land use on floods in relation to runoff and peak flows. Proc. California State Board of Forestry Meeting, February 26, 1965, pp. 47-52.